Motherhood, Medicine, and Me

Dr. Rebecca Levy-Gantt

Happy Reading!
Dr Rebecca Levy Gantt
:)

Motherhood, Medicine, and Me

ISBN: 978-1-941066-50-8

Book design by Jo-Anne Rosen

Cover design by Heather Belt

Wordrunner Press
Petaluma, California

Contents

Motherhood, Medicine, and Me

Preface

After writing my first book I was encouraged to put more of myself into the next one. My personal experience and my professional life are sometimes so intertwined that separation is impossible. Calling this book *Motherhood, Medicine, and Me* was an obvious choice. For my whole adult life, this is the order of importance I have placed on things: **Motherhood** has had first place from the moment I saw my firstborn after my unusually quick and unexpected delivery. I have tried to raise my children with support and unconditional love, even when I felt I was learning those things along with them. Motherhood is still my most important job: I now marvel at the independent and amazing adults those children have become.

Medicine has been a part of my life for most of the time I have been alive. Being part of the medical community is so completely connected to who I am that I don't think I know how to look at everyday things without a medical eye. I sometimes wish I could.

And **Me**: I have gotten better at taking care of myself and putting myself closer to first, but that's been a difficult and learned behavior. My first instinct has always been to be sure everyone else is okay before making sure **I** am. I now know self-care is important, and I often repeat this phrase to my family, friends, and patients: "If you don't take care of yourself, you can't take care of anyone else."

I am trying to heed my own advice.

This book does have more of *ME*. All the stories are true; some are composites. My hope is that the empathy, the sympathy, the laughter, and the tears that they provoke brings you into my world, where at the crossroads of motherhood and medicine, there's *ME!*

Placentas Can Be Jerks

Obstetrics is filled with emotional extremes. We experience the pinnacle of excitement on magical occasions, and the deep sadness and despair in tragedy. Sometimes both extremes happen for the same person. Caring for women and families who have found themselves at the opposite ends of the emotional spectrum can be difficult and exhausting.

A new patient, referred by another patient I had recently delivered, came to see me for an office visit. Ms. M was 32, tall, and healthy, and in the first weeks of her pregnancy. At the first prenatal visit, my practice is to get to know newly-pregnant patients in a long, leisurely consultation followed by a full exam, a discussion of pregnancy in general, and a talk about the particulars of planning for *her* healthy pregnancy. I introduced myself, and told Ms. M a little about our practice. She was quiet until I finished telling her that I was the only doctor in the practice and would be delivering her baby.

She then replied, "Good. That's what I'm looking for. I was going to a practice with lots of different doctors. I always saw someone different. They also never got back to me when I called to ask a question."

I hadn't known that Ms. M had sought prenatal care elsewhere. Looking at her I surmised she was still early in pregnancy. She wouldn't need multiple visits just yet unless, unless she had many medical problems or she made multiple appointments for concerns that did not necessarily require a visit. A discussion of doctors who don't answer or a decision to switch practices is sometimes a red flag. At that moment, I was glad we had time to discuss her history since this sounded like Ms. M was going to be different from my usual initial prenatal visit.

"Tell me a little about your history," I began, and then left the question open-ended so she could decide what she wanted to share.

"Well, I was pregnant last year after two years of trying. I found a group of doctors that was close to where I live, and had my prenatal care with them. Like I said, I never saw the same doctor twice, and sometimes when I called with a problem or question, I would have to wait a day or two before someone called me back. More than once, I never got a call back."

I listened but did not interject. I was used to hearing stories like this. Obstetrics was often practiced in large groups. The quality of life is better for doctors who share their schedule with many others. They know they will have regularly scheduled uninterrupted time each week. What gets lost in a large group practice, unfortunately, is for patients to feel a connection with any one particular doctor, often not knowing who will deliver their baby until the day they are in labor. As for not calling her back to answer questions, that might be bad management of phone calls, or the policy could be unless there's an emergency, calls are answered according to a particular schedule. I nodded, encouraging her to continue.

"Things seemed pretty normal; I had blood work and ultrasounds. I heard the heartbeat, and began to feel the baby moving at about four months. He was a boy. We painted the nursery and bought a crib with a butterfly mobile. We were so excited."

Here, Ms. M stopped. I watched as she was remembering these events so clearly and painfully. I tried to offer her comfort with quiet breathing, a hand on her shoulder, and a box of tissues as I saw her lower lip tremble and her shoulders start to slightly heave.

"And then," she continued, "I went for an office visit at 28 weeks, and they couldn't find the baby's heartbeat with that device, that doptone. I think that is what they called it. So they did an ultrasound, and my baby boy was dead."

At this moment, she let the tears flow. She buried her face in her hands with the tissues and sobbed. I had just met Ms. M, but this moment felt so intimate.

"Thank you for telling me about that. It must have been awful," I said.

And the two of us sat there for a couple of minutes, after which she said, "I'm ok. I'm really ok, but I couldn't go back there."

She didn't blame them. She just could not bring herself to return to a place that she associated with her sadness. Ms. M relayed the rest of her story, including how after another three months of trying after the last pregnancy ended, she and her husband decided to do in vitro fertilization so she could become pregnant again. She was currently at 10 weeks. Ms. M told me about her other medical history: she had a condition where her blood might not clot properly (low platelets), and her uterus was an odd shape, almost shaped like a heart. All that history added up to her being a very high risk pregnancy. And now she was coming to me.

When taking care of pregnant patients, I try to individualize care as much as possible: certain tests and specific plans need to be made for practically all prenatal patients, and others are tailored to each individual woman. Ms. M would need more frequent prenatal visits, and more than the usual number of ultrasounds to reassure her that the pregnancy was going well for her and her baby.

As we approached week 28, the week she suffered the devastating loss of her first baby, I saw Ms. M weekly and checked in on her almost daily. I offered a referral to a therapist if she wanted a professional to talk to about her fears and anxieties. The pregnancy was mostly normal. All the prenatal testing showed everything was on track for a healthy delivery and a healthy baby. The platelet levels were stable, and all the scans of her heart-shaped uterus showed no indication of a problem.

Ms. M and I had numerous conversations about the management of her pregnancy and delivery. I tried to balance the conversations between being as reassuring as I could while also making her aware of some of the complications that could potentially occur.

- Her platelet levels could start to go down, which may necessitate early delivery.
- Her abnormally-shaped uterus may not contract properly (called dysfunctional labor), and we may

need medications to help the uterus contract properly both for delivery and afterward.

- She may have preterm labor. Because of the shape of her uterus, the baby has less room to grow to full term.
- Sometimes in IVF pregnancies there is a tendency toward placental problems, either during pregnancy when the placenta doesn't supply the baby with enough nutrients to grow, or after the delivery when the placenta may get 'stuck' and not easily come out after the baby.

These were some of the complications that were specific to Ms. M. Of course, any delivery has the potential for all kinds of complications, and I wanted to be ready. The reality is that ready is never something we can completely be when delivering babies.

I saw Ms. M at her 36 week prenatal visit. Everything appeared normal. The baby was moving, the heart rate was in the expected range. Although she felt uncomfortable, there were no signs of labor. We made plans for her next weekly appointment. I made sure she knew how to get in touch with me after office hours.

Ms. M never made it to her week 37 appointment. A few days shy of that date, I was just finishing dinner when my phone rang. When I answered, I heard a breathless Ms. M on the other end.

"I think…... I may be…. going into labor," she haltingly said, stopping to take a breath between words. "The contractions started about three hours ago, and they're getting stronger."

She sounded surprisingly calm, but I recognized the sound of someone going into labor.

"Go right to the labor and delivery entrance at the hospital, and I'll meet you there soon," I told her.

Twenty minutes later I walked into the labor and delivery suite. Ms. M was in the room closest to the nurses' station. She was the only patient there. When I entered her room, I heard the buzz of activity that signaled an active labor patient. Ms. M was in a hospital gown, lying on her side in the bed, moaning softly. A glance at the monitor near the large window told me that the baby's heart rate was reassuring. Ms. M was having a strong contraction about every three minutes. I didn't have to look at the monitor to know that, as she was letting out longer and louder moans at three minute intervals, which crescendoed and de-crescendoed with the rounded peak of each contraction. Her face was flushed. She was sweating. Her husband sat next to her bed looking helpless. He had already been through a tragedy with her; now he watched his wife as her face contorted in pain. Except for a back rub or an offering of a water bottle, he could offer no assistance. I moved to the head of the bed to speak directly to her.

"It *does* look like you're in labor," I said, stating the obvious. "There's going to be a large flurry of activity around you now, asking questions and starting IV's, but I want to check your cervix to see how far along you are."

I was judging, from the frequency of her contractions and the loudness of the moans, that Ms. M was likely five or six centimeters dilated and well on her way to delivery. Her plan was to have an epidural for pain control, and this seemed the perfect time.

I got out my gloves and my lubricant as the nurses helped Ms. M get into a position on the bed where I could examine her between contractions. When there was a moment without moaning, I quickly checked her cervix and was pleasantly surprised to find her at eight centimeters dilated. She was closer to having her baby than I thought. If she truly wanted her preferred method of pain control, we would have to move quickly.

"Would you like to have that epidural we talked about?" I asked after announcing her advanced stage of dilation.

"Shit yes!" she said, loudly, right in the middle of the next contraction.

Several nurses appeared, taking care of the many tasks that needed doing to get a patient admitted and ready to deliver: asking so many questions, collecting the needed IV bags and tubing, and filling out consent forms.

I called the anesthesiologist, "I have a high risk patient at 8 centimeters who really wants an epidural. Think we can get this done as soon as possible?"

I was afraid that Ms. M would progress so quickly that if I did not make the call myself, by the time the anesthesiologist came in, it would be too late. Anesthesiologists are only required to be within 30 minutes of the hospital, and have that much time to respond to a call requesting that they come in. I thought that in thirty minutes Ms. M may have already delivered.

Luckily the anesthesiologist was more than happy to oblige. I was just hanging up the phone when Dr. A appeared at the delivery room entrance. I quickly explained the history, the tragic events of her last delivery, and her currently stable platelets. He got right to work, simultaneously explaining all the risks of epidural anesthesia while donning a sterile gown and gloves and getting all his medications together.

I have often wondered how much information a writhing, moaning 8-centimeter dilated woman can absorb, but that was not my concern at the moment.

She nodded her consent and signed the papers. Ms. M tried her best to stay still while Dr. A found his 'spot' in her lower spine. Within 10 minutes I saw that relieved, familiar look on Ms. M's face. She closed her eyes. Her breathing slowed. The moaning stopped.

"Enjoy that for a while," I said happily as I went out to the workstation to put all my notes and orders into the computer.

At about 9 in the evening, Ms. M pressed her call button. Her nurse and I both went into the room.

She told us, "I'm starting to have some pressure like I want to push."

I rechecked her cervix, and sure enough, it was 10 centimeters, or completely dilated, enough to start pushing the baby out. Women having their first baby can push up to three hours before we worry that they will be unsuccessful, so I only encourage pushing when there is a strong urge.

I usually stay with my patients throughout the whole pushing phase, encouraging and rooting them on as we get closer to delivery. As was fairly typical, I stayed with Ms. M to watch as she slowly eased the baby down the birth canal with every exhausting, concentrated push. After two and a quarter hours, little baby M emerged, soaking and bloody.

She had very little of that cheesy vernix, which usually covers a newborn's skin, as she was only 37 weeks along. Her cry was weak and her breathing was labored, so we called the neonatal doctor who was standing by to come take a look.

I clamped the umbilical cord, and Mr. M cut it. The baby was resting on Ms. M's chest. The placenta was still inside, with the portion of the cord still attached hanging down toward the floor.

While the neonatal doctor was examining baby M, and Ms. M and her husband were reveling in the surreal event that had just taken place, I sat on my delivery stool at the foot of her bed. Right before my eyes, something I had anticipated started to occur: large amounts of bright red blood were pouring out of the vagina, into the plastic bag which had been placed at the bed's edge, and onto the floor. At that moment, the possibilities went through my mind:

- Are there severe bleeding lacerations?
- Does this have to do with her abnormally shaped uterus that will not clamp down as usual and stop the bleeding?
- Are her platelets lower than I thought? Is her blood not clotting properly?
- Is the placenta to blame?

I went into automatic mode. Since I had thought this might happen, we had more than the usual number of nurses in the room, so we had more than the usual number of hands. I gave orders for various medications to help slow down the bleeding, and asked for assistance to place pressure on the areas of active bleeding. I could then see if and where I needed to stitch. The placenta remained inside the uterus, as it usually takes 15 minutes or so for the natural detachment of the placenta to occur. However, until the placenta comes out, it is difficult to completely assess the amount of bleeding and where it's all coming from, so in this situation, better out than in. I gave the umbilical cord a slight tug to see if I felt the usual 'give' of a placenta that is spontaneously detaching.

— Nothing.

I stitched all the bleeding areas that I could see externally so the blood flow from these areas would stop. I gave another small tug.

— Nothing.

I asked a nurse to massage Ms. M's abdomen, as sometimes a firm massage can encourage the placenta to detach.

— Nothing.

I reached further up into her cervix to see if the placenta was at least making its descent.

— Nothing.

At that point, 35 minutes from the delivery, with no placenta in sight, and constant blood now trickling, I decided to move into the operating room for the remainder of our delivery management. I updated Ms. M and her husband about my concerns. The neonatal physician took Baby M to the NICU for observation.

Mr. M followed the baby, but as he looked back over his shoulder he said, "Take care of her."

I nodded. Once in the OR, Dr. A injected more medication into the epidural and gave Ms. M some IV sedation.

I attempted to gently reach up into the uterus to find, grab, and remove the placenta.

The most important detail to remember in these cases is that the placenta must come out in one piece, in its entirety. If not, the risk is that parts of it remain inside, causing increased bleeding and possible infection. In preparation, I ordered IV antibiotics. I attempted to follow the umbilical cord and gently placed my hand through the still open cervix. Even though my hands are small, I could not get past the lower part of the uterus. I asked Dr. A to infuse a medication that would slightly relax the uterus so I could get inside. I knew this would inevitably cause more bleeding, as the uterus relaxed and the vessels that had previously been constricted started to dilate. I had no choice. The placenta had to come out. My adrenaline was rising.

The placenta is truly a remarkable organ. It develops in the uterus during pregnancy and acts like a two-way system for the growing baby. It provides oxygen and nutrients, and removes waste products from the baby's blood.

Placentas have more functions than just being the baby's blood supply and nutrition. They produce hormones and signaling molecules that the baby needs. These chemical messengers prepare the mother to make milk. Placentas have crucial work to do for those nine months. When their job is done, and the baby is delivered, most placentas 'know' exactly what to do.

Sensing they are no longer needed, they detach. They leave. They disappear, having provided the support that had been needed for 40 weeks, but not all of them know. Some decide to leave too soon. Some decide to grow in the 'wrong' place, and some don't know when their job is done and when to exit. Sometimes placentas can be jerks. That is what was going through my mind when I was trying to extract Ms. M's placenta. As the uterus started to relax a bit I could ease my right hand up inside the uterus.

"C'mon, c'mon," I repeated in my mind. "Release."

I willed the placenta to do the right thing. I tried to find the plane between the placenta and the uterine wall, but each time I slowly moved my fingertips upward, using the curled sweeping motion needed to gently detach the placenta in one piece, I felt nothing but mush. This meant that my fingers were likely just making holes in the placenta. Each time, I pulled back and tried a different direction, giving small tugs along the way. My left hand was on Ms. M's abdomen, massaging the top of her uterus. She was sleeping, sedated, and unaware of my now more-aggressive maneuvers to detach this placenta that wouldn't release.

I persisted, walking my first three fingers upward, searching for a plane. I was working hard, now sweating, narrowing my eyes, and concentrating, as the nurses and Dr. A looked on. Blood was still trickling. I ordered labs to be drawn to check how much Ms. M's blood count had actually gone down. I thought I may need to give her a blood transfusion.

"C'mon, placenta, you jerk," I whispered, crazily thinking I could reason with this organ that was clearly not responding.

I persisted. As I slightly turned my fingertips toward my left, I felt the bulk of the placenta with the palm of my hand. I gave one last slight tug. Suddenly I felt the 'plop' that signaled the placenta had detached! I steadied my hand, made sure I really had control of the placenta, and finally eased the entire thing out of Ms. M and into a specimen bowl.

I audibly sighed and said, "Thank you."

The surgical tech who had been standing behind me exclaimed, "Thank God."

I had to steady myself against the delivery table as I felt shaky. I ordered medications to again contract the floppy uterus, and the bleeding practically stopped. I looked at the clock: 2:30 in the morning. Five hours had passed since Ms. M had been admitted at 8 centimeters.

I finished my last few stitches, examined the placenta to be sure there were no missing pieces, and went to inform Mr. M about what had transpired. Ms. M would be awake soon, so I went to the workstation to document the events of the last several hours. She would likely have a difficult recovery, but all was well at the moment.

Several hours later, I walked into Ms. M's postpartum room. I was pleasantly surprised to see that she was sitting up in bed, eating breakfast. IV fluids and medications were running, a catheter was in her bladder, and an icepack was on her bottom. Her husband was on the recliner next to her. Her skin was pale, but she seemed awake and alert. Baby M was in a small bassinet next to her bed, sleeping. We had a lengthy discussion about everything that had happened and what to expect over the next few days while she recovered. She definitely realized that this had not been a run of the mill delivery, and some of the anticipated complications had been encountered and managed. She was grateful.

When we were done talking, I asked, "Did you have any other questions?"

Ms. M looked at me pensively, smiled, and said, "Yes, just one. I'm not sure if I dreamed this, but did I hear you call my placenta 'a jerk'"?

I was embarrassed, as I thought she was asleep when I whispered that, mostly to myself, in the OR several hours ago.

"Um, I may have said that, yes," I answered. "Sorry."

"Don't be sorry," she said, "*I totally agree.*"

Do as I Say, Not as I Do

I have never believed that physicians have to be personally diagnosed with the medical conditions they evaluate and treat in their patients to be effective practitioners. If *that* were the case, cardiologists could not be effective unless they had a heart condition, and gastroenterologists would have to have a stomach or bowel issue to appropriately diagnose and treat their patients.

As an obstetrician and gynecologist, I recently began to wonder if I am *not* a better and more effective physician specifically because I have experienced many of the things I evaluate and treat in my patients. When a woman tells me about her menstrual cramps, her contraceptive side effects, or her pregnancy-related symptoms and fears, I often find it hard *not* to utter the words, "Yes, I know exactly what you mean."

I realized long ago that information I convey to patients is more likely to impact their medical decision-making if that information is somehow attached to a personal anecdote. I am an evidence-based physician, which means I use relevant and up-to-date medical studies and information to advise patients on what their health outcomes are likely to be, given the choices they can make. When I review articles, discuss information with patients, and say, "This is what the science shows," I am often met with resistance. Pregnant patients in the ninth month hoping to soon go into labor almost always ask what they can do at home to move the process along. They never seem to believe me when I tell them that all the stories they have heard about eating dates and pineapple, taking long walks, and jumping up and down have no science behind them.

We are likely to have a continuing conversation where the patient believes that some information they *already knew*, or something someone has told them is as important and as likely to be true as my medical information and any scientific evidence I give them. This disconnect places me in a unique situation. I am a woman. I have experienced many of the things my patients have experienced, including menstrual symptoms, a need for contraception, various gynecological ailments, three pregnancies, three deliveries, and, now menopause.

I have been on both sides of the gynecological exam table and the delivery bed. These experiences have shaped my life as a woman and informed my work as a professional. I have thought a lot about how my experiences help me to be a better physician and to have more empathy for my patients. I ask myself if using my experiences would give patients better care.

As a solo ObGyn physician in private practice, I am afforded the luxury of sometimes having long conversations with patients. I get to know them well, precisely because I decide how much time to spend with them. I do not have to follow the ten minute rule, which is so common in large medical practices. I have the opportunity to explain my advice and thinking, and am able to at least try to be sure that our shared decisions are clear, understood, and usually written down, before a patient leaves my office.

I take care of a fair number of pregnant women. About half are having their first baby. There is so much information, counseling, and advice I like to, and need to, give to pregnant patients. I have started making sure that certain milestone visits have even more time allotted to discuss important pregnancy issues. Discussing genetic testing is not a ten minute conversation. Discussing complications like gestational diabetes or high blood pressure are not quick conversations. Talking about pregnancy nutrition and planning for a delivery takes more than fifteen minutes. I am glad to have that extra time.

I recently started adding my own pregnancy experiences into some of the conversations, discussing how various things affected me when I was pregnant and what *my* outcomes were. Without getting too personal, although I wonder what can be more personal than the story of giving birth to your own baby, I have realized when I include a bit of information about how I ate or how much I exercised, and what my delivery outcomes were, patients do take note.

I ask myself why. I am *not* a scientific study. I am an anecdote. Medical studies call these anecdotes an N of 1, meaning **one** person's information is included in the study, which is simply a non-study. I am one person who followed certain behaviors and had a good outcome three times, three live, healthy babies, who went home with me. And that seems to have more influence than any study I bring up, even if most of the outcomes were not in my control.

Is this a problem of a lack of understanding about how science works? Or is this just patients deciding they know me and trust me, so if I did something, then they might want to try to do the same? Again, this places me in a bit of a dilemma. I know that my one-person story should not be designed to try to change or influence my patients' behavior. I also do not want patients to put as much stock in what their relatives, their Facebook friends, their neighbors, or their colleagues tell them to do about their health care decisions: "I got an epidural and it was terrible!" Or, "I had no pain medication in labor, and everything was totally fine."

I want patients to trust the science. That means they trust the recommendations I give them. My recommendations are all from evidence-based studies and best-practice bulletins, as well as my 20 plus years of experience.

So what do I do?

I have to continue to offer my patients science. I explain, "In a large randomized controlled trial, women in the group who delivered in their 39th week of pregnancy had fewer cesarean sections than in the group of women who were allowed to pass their due date."

Someone telling a patient, "I passed my due date and everything was just fine," is neither evidence-based nor science-based. That is an anecdote.

I *must* continue to advise patients to make their medical decisions based on available evidence, so I can continue to give them the best care. I *may* still throw in anecdotes about my own life and my own outcomes, but I have to discourage the thinking that just because something happened to me, or something worked or didn't work for me, that same thing will also happen to you or work for you, no matter what you may be told or what you believe.

The truth is yes, I *am* on the same hormones I prescribe. I *do* take the supplements I recommend. I exercise the amount I recommend for my patients. And believe it or not, my first baby was born in the triage room at the hospital ten days before my due date because I had no idea I was in active labor. I walked in screaming and pushed three times. *I totally do not recommend that.*

Motherhood and Medicine, Part 1

Halfway through my second year of medical school, my husband and I moved from a small apartment to a house. Moving from one bedroom to a two story house in the same town seemed not too daunting a task, so we engaged our extended families and moved furniture and boxes, and more books than either of us had time to read. When we looked at our apartment's worth of furniture in our new big space, we realized what a huge undertaking this was and how much more work was facing us. We took two days to move everything in and start setting things up. At the end of the move, we realized we hadn't unpacked forks and pots, so we ordered New York-style pizza with extra mushrooms. I was never much of a pizza eater, maybe two slices.

That night I easily ate *four* slices of pizza, commenting, "This move must have had me working harder than I thought. I'm still famished!"

We looked at each other, and I went to the drugstore to buy a test. I knew from the pizza. I was pregnant. I still had seven months of my second year of medical school to go, which would end on June 30th. According to my calculations, my due date was August first. The planning was perfect. I would finish my second year of medical school while pregnant, deliver a few weeks later, and then stay home, on a leave of absence until I had the baby. I would take six months off and start my third year clinical rotations in January. Then I could go back and do my last two years of medical school, which consisted of hospital clinical rotations, and not be too far behind.

I thought "Who gets to stay home for six months with a baby?"

I felt lucky. Looking back, I cannot believe I was making major life choices and thinking I had some control over the timing of things. I had been raised to believe that if I could just control things, they would not scare me so much. Things are often not in my control, and sometimes all the planning in the world cannot change that. At the time, planning was the only thing I knew, my modus operandi.

My husband and I slowly got used to the idea that we would soon be parents. I was worried we might not have the same ideas when it came to parenting. I had more than my fair share of fears about continuing on my path to becoming a doctor, with a baby at home. How could I possibly do it, or have it, all? How would I feel when I knew I would have to be gone for long periods of time while pursuing my medical dream? These thoughts were always looming, but the desire to be a mother and a doctor were both so strong.

Luckily my pregnancy was uneventful. Not one sick day. I kept working, studying, taking tests, and planning. No one could even tell I was pregnant until about five months along. I approached an ObGyn physician who had come to give our class a lecture, asking if I could be his patient. He was more than accommodating.

I remember waiting *LONG* hours in his office for my appointments, and thinking to myself, "I will never work this way when *I* become a doctor!"

So many years later, as I am now in my own private practice, my goal has always been to be sure that patients do not spend a long time in my waiting room. I have been mostly successful, but that is not an easy task.

I finished my second year of medical school, at 36 weeks pregnant, and said goodbye to my classmates, as everyone was heading out in different directions. I would be staying home to await my delivery. My husband and I were getting ourselves and our home ready for the new baby. I had heard the horror stories about labor and delivery and pain and blood. I now had sufficient time to contemplate those narratives now that school was temporarily out. One evening when I was entering my 38th week, I felt very strong cramping, like menstrual cramps. My doctor had explained how to count the intervals between my contractions.

When they had been strong enough to take my breath away for more than an hour and coming regularly every five minutes, I thought, "Time to go to the hospital."

We arrived in the Labor and Delivery suite. I gave my information to the clerk. This was a teaching hospital, so I did not expect to find my doctor there waiting for me. Indeed he was not. Two nurses attached me to a monitor, making sure the baby's heart rate was reassuring. As I breathed with my contractions, one of the nurses checked me.

"You're 3 centimeters dilated. Too early to be admitted. Go back home. Take a shower, rest, and come back when things get stronger."

I don't think she called my doctor, but I did as she said. We lived 15 minutes from the hospital, and it was 4:30 in the morning. I assumed we would come back in a few hours. When we got home, I thought the shower might feel good. I got in, and the hot water eased the pain. About five minutes into what felt like relief, I heard and felt a pop.' A gush of clear fluid was released onto the shower mat. Before I had time to contemplate that this must have been my water breaking, I started to feel some serious lower abdominal pains that I could only describe as the sensation that the lower half of my body was about to explode.

I yelled to my husband, "We need to go back, *NOW*!"

I don't know how my husband got me into the car. He drove back to the hospital, ignoring all the red lights. We were back at that Labor and Delivery suite at 5:45, in just ten minutes. I am sure I scared the heck out of him with the sounds coming out of my mouth as the contractions became stronger and stronger. We walked, me just barely, back into the same exam room, with the same nurse. She greeted me with an expression I could only interpret as, 'You again?'

The nurse gave me a gown. I slowly made my way to the curtained dressing room. When I got there, I sat on the floor, crying in pain. My husband threw the curtain back, picked me up, and eased me back down on the exam table.

I remember begging, "If this is three centimeters, *please* give me some pain medication!" The resident was there in two seconds.

After she checked my cervix, she said, "Nope, no pain medicine, just push!"

All I remember from that moment was screaming and pushing. Was that me screaming? Then, surprisingly, my ObGyn, in his street clothes, came running into the room, just in time to catch my baby on the third push. Everything became quiet, the surreal calm after the storm. I looked at Jake's dark wet hair and started to cry those tears of love and confusion. What had just happened? My delivery was *nothing* like I had heard about first babies. I had no time for pain meds, no time for a birth plan, and almost no time for my doctor to get there.

Jacob entered the world before I even got to a labor bed, before my doctor could change into scrubs. This was my first experience with obstetricians discarding perfectly good clothes when showered with the inevitable fluids of labor. I have been there many times.

Jake must have been anxious to arrive! And nothing I had done, seen, learned, or read had adequately prepared me for how I felt, a deep, overwhelming love for this tiny, beautiful baby. I would have done anything to ease his pain, to make him happy, to entertain him, and to make sure he knew I was there for him. I couldn't remember or imagine what life was like before his arrival.

I Always Go in at 4:00 in the Morning

One Saturday, on an otherwise pretty quiet on-call weekend as an attending physician, the piercing ring of my phone, which, as usual, was strategically placed next to my head, wrenched me out of sleep at 4:00 in the morning.

"Hello. Dr. Levy here," I answered, trying to sound like I had *not* just been pulled out of a coma.

"It's Anna, from Labor and Delivery. An ambulance pulled up a few minutes ago, and a patient, 38 weeks pregnant, came in, with severe left lower quadrant pain."

"OK, any other history?" I asked.

"Yes, she's had two prior C-sections, and just woke up with severe pain and called an ambulance."

Anna said all this sounding annoyed — at me? At my questions? At the patient? At the use of ambulances? I couldn't tell.

"The pain is all the way around to her left flank. So maybe it's a kidney stone?"

I was wide awake now.

Skilled labor and delivery nurses are invaluable. They are the first contact when pregnant women walk, or are wheeled, into the delivery room. Having an experienced nurse make that initial assessment can be the difference between me running to the hospital at full speed and allowing a slower evaluation for something less emergent. I didn't know this nurse well enough to trust her opinion on a possible kidney stone. A story with an ambulance, severe pain, and two prior C-sections was enough to get me running to the hospital.

When I got there, I heard loud moaning coming from the labor room that was closest to the nurse's station. This moaning was similar to what I had heard hundreds of times before when a woman was in labor, close to delivering: heavy breathing, moaning louder and louder, then after a minute or so quiet, until the whole sequence resumed. This woman's moans were pretty startling. I began formulating possible diagnoses in my head even before I went into the labor room. Either she was in active labor close to having a delivery, or something was very wrong. When I walked into the room, my racing thoughts focused.

I immediately poked my head out of the labor room, just long enough to tell the nurse at the desk, "Open the OR. Now please."

Maybe I didn't say please. I went over to the patient, Ms. L was curled up in a fetal position on her right side, sweating, rocking, and moaning. I still had to do my entire evaluation.

I quickly explained: "Hi, I'm Doctor Levy. I'm on-call tonight. I'm worried about the amount of pain you're having. With two prior C-sections, it is definitely possible that the scar in your uterus is opening up, what we call a 'uterine rupture.' That's what's so painful. This is an emergency. We need to do a C-section as soon as possible."

This was in my calmest-but-really-shitting-in-my-pants voice. I was directing the nurses to place two large IVs in her arms, and give Ms. L medication, looking at the fetal monitor strip, which until now showed a normal fetal heart rate. I was doing my exam and getting her history, and at the same time I was trying to explain the need to do a C-section to Ms. L. When I gently placed my palm on the left lower part of her abdomen, Ms. L jumped away from me and screamed.

The deal was sealed. The most likely diagnosis was uterine rupture. We needed to *move*. The patient, looking scared, sweating, and in horrific pain, described haltingly what had happened over the last hour. She was sleeping. She woke up with severe pain, went to the bathroom, started vomiting, and could not stand up again. Her husband called an ambulance. She also mentioned she was supposed to have come to the office last week to schedule her elective repeat C-section, but she hadn't made it to that appointment.

Anesthesia and the OR were ready in minutes. I called Dr. R to assist me. He lived close to the hospital and was always willing to be there in an emergency. Ms. L was wheeled into the OR. This was not the first, and would not be the last, time I was about to open an abdomen, uncertain what I would find.

As usual, my heart was racing. I was sweating. I stayed focused on the list of things I would need to remember: which medications to give in which order if we couldn't stop the bleeding; which special instruments we may need; and how this might be different from the many C-sections I'd already done.

I made the incision in the abdomen and noted a significant amount of scar tissue since Ms. L had had two other C-sections. I used my knife all the way down to the muscle layer. Across the table from me, Dr. R assisted. We pulled the muscles outward. Just as we got to the peritoneal layer, we saw a tiny arm already out of the uterus, poking through the area where I would normally have needed my knife to reach the baby. The entire scar in the lower segment of the uterus was open. The baby was right there, without me using a knife at all. I scooped him up, clamped the cord, and handed Baby L to the pediatric team next door in the neonatal intensive care unit. The night nurses were ending their shift, but the bright lights were on, and the equipment was beeping. The neonatal unit was ready for anything.

Once we removed the placenta and got a good look, we saw the uterus was like a wet, bleeding rag, and spouting bright red blood from multiple places. I started to sew everything closed as fast as possible, but the more stitches I placed, the more the blood would spurt from other areas in the muscle tissue. I ordered medications to slow the bleeding. We were still elbow deep in a puddle of blood after several doses.

My adrenaline was rising. I ordered blood to be ready for transfusion if we needed it. The list of things that can stem the bleeding tide had a few more choices, including cutting off the blood supply to the uterus by ligating major arteries and ultimately, completely removing the uterus, meaning a hysterectomy. We weren't there yet.

I remembered a special stitch I read about. An article in a medical journal had a step-by-step guide on how to place a special compression stitch around the uterus when all else had failed: a stitch I had never placed, but one designed to encircle the uterus in a particular way and create compression. The compression was to block the blood supply feeding the uterus.

I asked for the suture on the 'biggest needle,' and proceeded to place the compression stitch as I had remembered it in the article: in and out vertically on the front of the uterus, over the top of the uterus, in and out on the back, back over the top, in and out again, and then tie it in front in a tight surgeon's knot.

We waited. I compressed the uterus between my hands while continuing to order an array of medications to help the uterus contract. All sound in the room had ceased. The anesthesiologist signaled that the patient's vital signs were still stable. After what seemed like an eternity, but was only ten minutes, the bleeding decreased to a slow trickle.

I placed the uterus back into the abdominal cavity and continued the closure. I felt relieved but still anxious when I got to the last layer. Everyone, Dr. R, the anesthesiologist, and the two nurses, heard the click-click-click of the stapler as I closed the skin. We placed a bandage on Ms. L, counted all the instruments to confirm that in our haste and after all the bleeding that nothing was left behind. We moved out of the OR. Mom and baby were stable. I finished my notes, wrote the orders, and went home, exhausted, sweaty but feeling accomplished. I had just enough time for oatmeal with a banana before I had to get to the office for my first patient.

On the counter next to the coffee pot was my stack of journals. On top was the one with the article that described

"How To Place a B-Lynch Compression Suture." I chuckled, thinking how glad I was to have read about that stitch. Serendipity.

Motherhood and Medicine, Part 2

In the spring of my fourth year of medical school, while on a required medicine rotation, I was feeling my usual medical-student symptoms: hungry all the time, extreme fatigue, slight dizziness after a long shift, and more than a little irregular. A quick test in the lounge bathroom confirmed what I thought. I was pregnant again!

I had given birth to my son Jake at the end of my second year in medical school, and then stayed home with him for six glorious months. That put me six months behind my class, but that didn't matter much since the third and fourth years were all clinical clerkships. We rotated to a different specialty every four or six weeks. As long as I did the required clerkships, I would still graduate, albeit later than originally planned. This was perfect. As long as I stayed healthy, had no pregnancy complications, and could tolerate the hospital odors, I could make it through graduation, sans diploma. I would continue through six more months of my clerkship rotations. Then I could give birth to my baby and take another six months off before starting my residency, hopefully in ObGyn.

When I stayed home after the birth of my son, those six months were so important. I was learning to be a mother, trying to figure out both of our schedules, breastfeeding, and bonding with Jake. To be able to do that again would feel like heaven. I would finish medical school and have two babies, all in five years. That was me, optimistically planning.

No one knew I was pregnant.

My clerkship rotation in May, the last one before the graduation ceremony, was four weeks in reproductive endocrinology and infertility.

"How ironic," I thought.

Although I thought helping couples achieve a pregnancy would be in the happy part of obstetrics and gynecology, the reality was the opposite. Reproductive endocrinology and infertility was one of my saddest fourth year rotations.

Watching women and their partners go through cycle after cycle of fertility treatments, ovarian stimulation, egg retrievals, surgeries, procedures, and medications was neither happy nor satisfying. All were aimed at achieving a successful pregnancy and ultimately having a baby. The reality was that many ended in failure. Seeing those repeated failures was difficult to watch. When each menstrual cycle is seen as another failed pregnancy, when people bear the incredible expense of doing more in an effort to become parents, yet few do, I could not help feeling guilty about how easy becoming pregnant was for me.

I was grateful not to be showing and not to have morning sickness. The two and a half month pregnancy was my secret. Just didn't feel right being pregnant while the women I saw rarely achieved a successful pregnancy. I wanted to avoid causing any patient more pain and suffering. Participating in counseling sessions with these women was heartbreaking and difficult since I believed I could not understand what they were going through.

Then I had an epiphany. Being able to care for and treat patients depended *not* on whether I had actually experienced what they were experiencing. Treating them depended not only on my ability to be professional and provide the best medical advice and counseling, but to empathize with them, to place myself in their shoes, and to listen to them, to do what *I* would have wanted from my doctor if I were in their place. Looking at practicing medicine from this perspective became my mantra. I wanted to be the physician I would want and need if I walked in their shoes.

I made it without complications through early June, and went to my graduation ceremony with my original medical school class. While I realized graduation was a significant accomplishment, I couldn't exactly feel the way my classmates did since I wasn't actually done. I was six months behind everyone.

At the graduation ceremony, I realized many of us had not seen each other in months, as we were scattered on different clerkship rotations, in different hospitals, and sometimes in different parts of the country. Some of our original classmates were missing. Some had dropped out during the last two years; one had passed away. I had heard some stories from my classmates: Two students decided that medicine was not their calling, one went back to school to study law, and one had started an acting career. A few reportedly could not pass their third year rotations and had been asked to leave. The majority of my medical school class was present. Most did not know I wasn't finishing the year with the class. I thought I looked pretty pregnant, but no one could tell that under my graduation gown was a maternity dress. My mother, husband, and son were at the graduation ceremony. They were beaming. Many people didn't know I had had a baby in my second year until they saw Jake, who was almost two, in my arms.

People commented: "Amazing! I had a hard enough time just getting through the rotations, and you had a baby in the middle of all that?"

I suspect they were half in awe and half assuming that I was insane. Looking back now, I see that mine was an unusual plan, but at the time I thought I was being practical. I was getting older, and wanted at least two kids. Those kids had to happen sometime, and had to be planned. So far, I thought all was going according to my schedule. I hadn't given much thought to the fact that I was incredibly lucky to have become pregnant when I did, and to have a healthy first pregnancy and normal delivery. When people commented, I could think of nothing but how wonderful it was to focus on just that.

After graduation I was back to medical school reality with a pediatric rotation, with time in the Neonatal Intensive Care Unit (NICU). I had arranged the rotation because I was kind of afraid of the NICU on some of my other rotations. I needed to push myself past my comfort zone, and be around small babies, sick babies, scary babies, with the many things that could and did go wrong in those early days and weeks of life. If I was eventually going to be involved in the care of women delivering babies, babies that might need special care, I wanted to peek into the world that these women and their babies would inhabit. Quite alarming was realizing that some of the babies in the NICU were almost the same gestation as the one inside me.

The rotation through the NICU was as scary as I anticipated. This was the same hospital where I had given birth. Although Jake did not need to go into the NICU, I did know some of the nurses, medical students, and residents from my other rotations, or from other parts of my life. This rotation included staying overnight in the hospital twice a week, and many NICU emergencies took place in the middle of the night.

The smallest babies in the NICU were no older than 24 weeks gestation. Thirty-seven weeks and beyond is considered full term. These micro preemies and the older babies had all sorts of medical problems. Their day-to-day lives in the NICU were touch-and-go. I will never forget the nights when tiny babies, babies that would fit into the palm of my hand, emergently needed life-saving care when it seemed their organs were failing. With so many tubes and medications and procedures, their medical issues sometimes seemed incompatible with life, or at least, with a good life.

Everyone connected to each tiny baby—the mother, the family, the students, the nurses, and the pediatrician—faced a dilemma. Did parents want everything done? Did they understand the kind of life they were going to have with a gravely ill premature baby? And how much guilt and fear do they all carry?

These decisions often involved not only the parents and medical professionals, but also counselors, clergy, and the hospital bioethics committee. I wondered how I would deal with a similar situation. I learned so much each day about how lucky parents were who had low risk pregnancies and deliveries, about how many things could go wrong, and about the difficulties deciding what to do for these tiny babies when things did go wrong. I thought more and worried more about my own baby.

I was also in the process of choosing an obstetrician for my own pregnancy. I was considered low risk. I was young and healthy, having had not only a prior healthy pregnancy, but an easy delivery two years earlier. Possibly because I was seeing so much high risk activity in the hospital, I wanted as low risk an experience as possible. I found a local obstetrician through a friend's recommendation. Dr. L had a solo ObGyn practice, so I knew exactly who would be delivering me. I loved the idea that he and his staff knew me and got to know my family although I certainly did not understand how someone could work alone as an ObGyn.

This was an unpredictable life. How did he see his family? How did he take vacations? Did he get enough sleep? Was he still enjoying his specialty after so many years? I made a note-to-self to ask him these questions during my visits. My aim was to sock away his responses for the future. Dr. L delivered at a community hospital, where they only took care of low risk babies and moms who made it beyond 35 weeks of gestation. My visits were low key. I asked my questions and got to know everyone in the office, had all my blood work done, and was hoping and planning for a normal, uneventful delivery somewhere around the end of the year.

My next rotation was one I was looking forward to, an ObGyn clinic rotation. The clinic was close to my house. If not for the late August New York heat and humidity and if I had not been pregnant, I could have walked the mile to the clinic every morning and the mile home every night. The rotation was daytime hours only, which I so appreciated after the NICU. Sleeping between unexpected night time events during the NICU rotation had not been easy. I cherished going home at the end of the day and seeing my husband, Jake, and my own bed and pillows.

The ObGyn rotation, which included seeing a large variety of pathology, was at the biggest public hospital on Long Island. This was a place I would highly consider doing my residency if I liked the program, and if the people in the program liked me. The rotation was, like many of the other fourth year rotations, four weeks, starting in late August. I was five months pregnant, and the pregnancy and the rotation were going well. I was seeing all kinds of patients in the clinic: pregnant women for prenatal visits; women who needed a general checkup, Pap smear, birth control, or treatment for an infection; women suffering from painful conditions and infertility; and women needing surgery.

I was a meticulous note-taker, everywhere carrying yellow lined paper, spiral notepads, and small notebooks with alphabetized sections. I wrote down everything from how to use the hospital intercom system to which birth control pill contained which dose of which hormone. I was prone to drawing pictures when I was trying to educate or explain details to patients. I could illustrate my explanations of 'What is a Pap smear and why do you need one?' and draw a simple picture of a uterus with various anatomical problems. I became famous for my ability to draw a picture upside down while patients were sitting in front of me. For them, the drawing would appear right side-up. I was able to do patient clinic visits by myself since attendings and upper level residents were around to consult or give advice when students needed input.

The clinic was crowded: people standing in lines, sitting on beige plastic chairs, older people sleeping. Signs in English and Spanish directing patients to radiology and dermatology were everywhere. People moved back and forth. The entire scene was a bit chaotic, but I was doing so much patient care and learning so much. I was getting a handle on how to examine, consult, and treat patients.

Even though the scene seemed chaotic, we medical students knew the unwritten clinic rules. I learned to (1) avoid anything that would create more work for the residents, (2) do everything to make the lives of the residents easier, and (3) never contradict the residents, especially in front of patients or attendings. I had one rule of my own: finding residents who were doing things the way that made the most sense to me, treating patients how I would want to be treated. My plan was to follow *these* residents and learn, so I could do what they did.

More than once I heard this advice from the better residents: "It doesn't matter how you decide you are going to do it. Just get a method and stick to it, so that you never miss anything."

I created a new patient checklist. When I saw a patient, I would be sure to get a complete history and exam, checking off all the items on my list before declaring the visit over. This approach to having my own method was logical, and played right into my sense of wanting everything to be orderly and complete. I wanted to make sure I did not miss the history of complicated pregnancies and deliveries, medical problems, allergies, and even marital and relationship history. I wanted to **know** my patients.

The clinic was staffed with residents who were just trying to finish their shift from the night before and go home to sleep. Midwives and PAs were trying to give good care to the mostly poor, underserved patients, and students like me were just trying to take it all in and figure out how to learn and survive the next few weeks.

I was trying to enjoy my pregnancy while working full time, absorbing all I could about how to become a proficient physician, an adequate wife, and a capable mother. I was unsure if I was accomplishing any of that, but I was having an amazing time trying.

The Push and Pull of a Delivery

One procedure I mastered in the delivery room during my residency was the instrumental delivery. This was used for a woman attempting to deliver vaginally if she couldn't push the baby out because of exhaustion, or when an emergent event occurred, which meant the baby needed to be delivered right away. A fetal heart monitor indicates fetal distress if the oxygen supply to the baby is being compromised. I could then use either a vacuum device or a pair of forceps to quickly extract the baby. Becoming an expert in these types of deliveries in a training program required doing as many as possible, in slightly-less-than emergent circumstances, so that when true emergencies occurred, I would be ready.

Over the four years of my residency, whenever a patient was a candidate for a delivery assisted by forceps or a vacuum device, as junior residents, we would be encouraged to practice doing these procedures to be sure we could do them correctly, efficiently, and completely. We were taught that there were absolutely deliveries that *could* be assisted by instruments, and there were those deliveries that *needed* to be assisted by instruments. If we learned from the former, then we could best help the latter. A correctly-placed set of forceps during a delivery can be a lifesaving procedure.

A teaching institution is designed to do exactly that—teach. Fewer physicians know how to use forceps because not enough older doctors are in practice to teach younger doctors the correct method. Patients would end up being delivered by cesarean if no one could do a safe forceps delivery. I was lucky to have done more than 200 of these deliveries by the time I was near the end of my residency. I felt ready to use the instruments whenever emergently needed.

One night during my fourth year in residency, I was on a break in the on-call room. The other more junior residents were as usual in charge of the delivery room. Several patients were in labor, and deliveries occurred every two or so hours. One woman, Ms. K, was having her third baby, which usually meant the delivery would go smoothly. She had been pushing for almost an hour when a junior resident, Dr. G, called me to come to the back delivery room, where he was attending the delivery. The top of the baby's head was visible at the opening to the vaginal area when the patient pushed, but in between the pushes the head would sneak back up inside.

We assessed the situation. Ms. K was overweight, pushing in a back-lying, knees-to-her-chest position, which I always thought seemed counter-intuitive, to go against gravity. She looked exhausted. Her other two babies were small at birth: one was six and a half pounds and the other seven. Looking at her belly, this baby seemed bigger. His heart rate monitor was beginning to show signs he was being somewhat stressed with each contraction, decreasing from the reassuring rate of 140 into the double digits pretty consistently. This was a warning. All was not going well.

Dr. G looked at me and excitedly asked, "Do you think we can use instruments?"

As was my task to educate him, I responded, "Where's your checklist?"

All doctors know to safely consider a vacuum or forceps for a delivery, certain things had to be checked off on a list, which was usually in my head, but sometimes on paper as well. Dr. G started to list them out for me.

"Tested pelvis? Yes." (She had had vaginal deliveries before.)

"Adequate anesthesia? Yes." (She had an epidural.)

"Baby in the right position and at the right station? Not quite yet." (The baby had to be visible at the introitus between pushes as well, not just during pushes. That was at what was called the +2 or +3 station to safely put instruments on.)

"Informed consent? Not yet."

The resident had to explain the risks and benefits of using instruments on the baby to Ms. K. She could then decide if she wanted to allow instruments. This was a step I had definitely seen unchecked on the list more than once.

"Estimate of the baby's size? Yes." (This baby looked about eight pounds from the measurements.)

After these and the other checklist questions, I asked the nurses to set up for a forceps delivery. I called the anesthesiologist to come into the room. Ms. K pushed a bit more. The resident had the consent discussion with her.

After the discussion Ms. K said, "Yes, please, just get him out!»

Criteria were met, and I went into teaching mode. The nurse brought in my favorite Tucker McClean forceps. I showed Dr. G how to hold the first blade, as my chief resident taught me years before.

"Your left blade goes on first, hold it like it's just hanging down, use your thumb to gently slide it into position along the baby's temple. Then just let it sit. Now for the other blade. Again, let it hang. Then use your right thumb to gently arc the blade, and slide it into place on the baby's other temple. If the two blades are in the right place, they should easily lock, without putting pressure on the baby's skull."

I showed Dr. G how to sit and position himself to gently ease the baby's head out over the perineum while directing the mom's pushing efforts. With our gentle traction, out popped the baby's head, looking slightly sideways at an angle to the floor. We looked at each other with relief. After we put the blades down and tried to deliver the shoulders, we realized the rest of the baby was not following. He was stuck! The head sat there, with its chubby cheeks, and what looked like very little room around his neck. The shoulders were stuck inside behind the pelvic bone.

This is a shoulder dystocia, a true emergency. Having had more than a bit of experience with dystocias, my mind immediately went into automatic mode. I had the nurses position the patient with her knees bent in the extreme, flexed onto her large belly. I called for a nurse to climb up onto a step stool and put pressure over the pubic bone in the direction of the impacted shoulder. Once the two quick-acting, experienced nurses completed these maneuvers, I was able to then slightly turn the baby and deliver the body, after what seemed like forever but in actuality was about 20 seconds.

Once the baby came out, nurses whisked him away to the nursery to attend to his big floppy body. I braced myself on the instrument table and breathed heavily for another 20 seconds.

I looked at the junior resident and said, "Whenever you intervene with instruments because a baby doesn't want to come out, realize there may have been a reason he wasn't coming out. Be ready for anything."

Dr. G looked at me with a combination of elation that he had just done his first forceps delivery, and recognition that this could have been a complete disaster if we had not acted so quickly. Anything can happen at any time during a delivery. I repeated that for the resident and for myself. We have to be ready, all the time. The baby, except for some initial diminished movement in his right arm, was ultimately fine. Whew!

I looked back at the patient's bottom. We had used instruments, and done a lot of maneuvering to get the baby out. Ms. K was now in for a long repair job. I brought over my stool and sat down. As much as I loved teaching residents, and especially teaching the fine art of a forceps delivery and how to handle a shoulder dystocia, I was now about to teach my most unfavorite lesson. Dr. G and I were going to have an hour-long session on how to repair a major tear of the perineum.

I Wasn't That Special

When I worked in a group practice, pregnant patients would see all four of the doctors for their office visits. A bond would sometimes form between a patient and a particular doctor, and that patient would request that doctor for all her visits. This was not encouraged.

For us, the enormous advantage of a group practice was the shared responsibility for patient care. When a patient went into labor, she'd be familiar and comfortable with all the physicians, any of whom might be on-call to attend the labor. A patient would occasionally ask me to 'special' her, so when she did go into labor, I would agree to be paged even if I was not on-call that particular night. I agreed to this relationship once in a while and enjoyed that extra bond with those women. I tried not to agree too often, as then I would never be able to take advantage of those nights when my life was my own.

I was a few years into my employment with three other doctors in a busy private practice in New York. Ms. X had seen me for almost all her prenatal care. She was 28, having her first baby. She was healthy but extremely anxious. She needed a lot of extra explanations and reassurances that things happening during her pregnancy were normal and expected.

We had numerous long conversations about pregnancy, labor, and delivery. I enjoyed talking to her because she listened to the information and took notes, bringing up topics we had discussed at earlier visits. She was a teacher. I was from a whole family of teachers, so we had things in common. I readily agreed when she asked if I would 'special' her delivery, promising to be the doctor coming to the hospital when she went into labor. My saying yes put her at ease.

Ms. X's pregnancy progressed normally. Her ultrasound revealed she was having a boy. I never met her husband because he never accompanied her to her prenatal visits. That was unusual, but Ms. X said he worked long hours.

At 36 weeks, about eight months along, I did my usual office ultrasound to check the baby's position, size, and amniotic fluid level. The baby was in a head down position, and at an appropriate size at almost six pounds. I would normally measure the amniotic fluid levels by checking the various fluid pockets around the baby. I noted the fluid level was mildly low. I also noted Ms. X's blood pressure was 130 over 85. This was the first time her blood pressure was higher than normal.

Ms. X was certain she was just feeling extra anxious that day, and told me it was nothing to worry about. I discussed all the possibilities with her. I told her if her blood pressure continued to be high, this could impact the baby's growth and well-being and her health. If Ms. X had high blood pressure and other signs, like swelling, protein in her urine, abdominal pain, or symptoms, like a headache, then she might be becoming preeclamptic. She would then need to be delivered soon.

I advised her to have blood work done and come to the office for more frequent prenatal visits. We would evaluate whether this was an emerging problem. She seemed more anxious at each visit, but I felt we were keeping close watch. We would frequently discuss the possible plans for early delivery if her symptoms were to worsen, or if my comfort level waned.

At Ms. X's next few visits, her blood pressure continued to be elevated, and at 38 weeks, she had marked swelling in her hands and feet. I recommended that now was the time to be admitted to the hospital to induce labor. The benefit of continuing her pregnancy did not outweigh the risk of leaving the baby in an environment that was becoming un-safe. She seemed reluctant, but assured me she would speak to her husband. She said we would talk later that day. I tried to make clear that this was my absolute recommendation for the health and safety of her and her baby. Two and a half hours passed. I did not hear from her. I then called her. Ms. X answered. I repeated my concerns.

She said, "I'm helping my sister now, but I'll be home soon. I'll call you back then."

I thought her response odd, and immediately sensed I hadn't made myself clear. I was not in the habit of using words to frighten pregnant women into following my plans for their labor and delivery. I believed that my patients would understand my explanations, and that we would make joint, safe decisions on how to proceed after I had presented them with medical evidence and options. I thought when I had a relationship with a patient for at least the last nine months, she would trust me.

She would realize that my main interest would be helping her have a safe delivery. I didn't use phrases like 'Your baby could die' when making my recommendations. I avoided those words with Ms. X, but I tried to make her risks clear.

On the call with Ms. X, I said, "High blood pressure and low fluid is not something to treat expectantly. It would be much better for you and your baby to be somewhere that I can monitor you, and get your labor going in a safe environment."

Ms. X abruptly responded, "I'll call you."

The line went dead. I didn't know what to think. Her response was out of character. Although anxious, she had never been short with me. I didn't know what else to do. I waited. When more than an hour went by, I called her number again. I was worried, and determined to somehow explain in a way that would convince her she should follow my plan. I reached a voicemail on the other end.

Ms. X's voice said, "Leave a message at the sound of the tone."

I spoke to her voicemail and said, "This is Dr. Levy. I am very worried about you, and thinking I haven't made myself clear. Let me do so now: you have high blood pressure and swelling with low fluid around the baby. You are possibly suffering from preeclampsia, which we discussed before. This is dangerous for you and your baby. You should not remain pregnant. You could have a seizure. You could put the baby at risk. Please call me, or just come to the hospital now."

I had done my best to leave a message conveying my concern. I left her my number and hung up, now more than a little puzzled and more anxious for her and her baby.

About an hour later, my phone rang. When I picked up, I was surprised to hear a man speaking on the other end. I was hoping Ms. X would be calling back, on her way to the hospital.

"This is Mr. X," he said in a curt monotone.

This was obviously my patient's husband, the man I had never met.

Before I could say a word, he continued, "We have decided to seek other care. We are not interested in coming in for the induction of labor. We have a different plan."

I just about fell off my chair. I began to protest, but he gave me no chance to answer. He hung up. My head was spinning. I had so many simultaneous thoughts that I did not know which one should direct me to action. The main thought that was actually screaming in my brain was, what in the hell did I just hear?

I was still thinking maybe I had not been crystal clear in my explanation. Maybe they didn't get the urgency of this situation. Then I slowly realized maybe something else was going on. I had never met him. I did not know what their relationship was like. Was her husband forcing her into some decision that wasn't hers? Was Ms. X somehow a captive? Was someone else having undue influence on her? Was she safe? And where was she?

I remembered then that I had a non-professional connection to someone in this patient's family. A friend of mine was a cousin of this patient's stepmother. At the beginning of her pregnancy, when we realized that connection, we thought what a small world New York was, that I knew someone who was somehow related to her. We never mentioned that connection again. Of course, I had never told my friend I was taking care of a distant family member of hers. Medical privacy laws are specific and strong. I would never have breached those rules, but now I believed Ms. X was in danger. The only option was to try to reach her in any way I could, privacy laws be damned.

I called my friend, and said, "I know this is really unusual, but I am worried about Ms. X."

I summarized my previous four hours, asking if she could call to check on her cousin's stepdaughter, and see if there was something I was missing. This sounded crazy to me. While I was explaining to my friend, I felt awkward. She said she would call her cousin. My friend called back in ten minutes. Even though this event happened years ago, I remember her exact words as if she were speaking today.

"Ms. X told her stepmom that you knew she was planning to deliver at home, in a birthing tub, under the care of a home-birth midwife, and that you were coordinating care with the midwife. You and the midwife are working together."

My jaw dropped. I had never been so stunned to hear a piece of information over the phone, being delivered to me by a friend, information that had no basis in reality. I had to take a minute to absorb what I was hearing.

In my shock, the only thing I said to my friend was, "That is completely untrue. I have no idea what she's talking about."

I again mouthed, *what in the hell is going on?*

At that moment, I was not sure whether I felt angrier at the planned deceit that had been taking place over the last few weeks and hours, or at the flagrant disregard for me, my medical knowledge, my concern, my interest in her well-being, and my time. What ultimately emerged as the strongest emotion of the moment was how utterly and absolutely hurt I felt. Until this moment I had thought I had a professional partnership with a patient I cared for, one where I was guiding her toward shared decision-making based on the best medical evidence I had for her health, safe labor, and delivery.

Everything changed when I understood she had no regard for my expertise. She chose to deceive me so she could try for the delivery she wanted without telling me, a delivery that did not involve me. If her plan did not work out, I was being kept in the dark so I could possibly be there to bail her out of a difficult situation. Had I not found out about her plans from my friend, I would still have been obligated to participate in her delivery if she showed up at my hospital. All I could think about was how hurt I was.

I immediately called Ms. X's number. Again, I got her voicemail. This time, however, after the beep, I *was* crystal clear.

I said, "I have heard you are planning to deliver at home. Now this makes sense to me. I want to be clear. Your plan is against my medical advice for many reasons, most of all because you have risk factors that make you too high risk to consider a home delivery. Your blood pressure is high, and your fluid level is low. I am disappointed you decided not to tell me the truth about your plans. This also means as of right now, I am not your obstetrician. If you have a complication at your home delivery and require hospital care, you will be in the hands of an on-call doctor from Labor and Delivery. I repeat, you will not see me at the hospital."

I recorded this conversation and then transcribed it onto paper to be placed in Ms. X's chart in my office the next day. With all the thoughts racing through my mind, the question of liability was prominent.

I then called the delivery room at the hospital where Ms. X was not planning to deliver. Staff at the hospital were used to patients who had attempted home birth only to encounter complications—hemorrhage, fevers, infections, damaged babies—and then needed to be transferred to the hospital emergently.

I told the charge nurse in the delivery room that a patient who had previously been mine was attempting a home birth against my advice. Although my name was attached to the patient's prenatal records, I was no longer responsible for this patient. If she showed up at the hospital, staff should contact the on-call hospitalist group to attend to this patient's care. As a courtesy I called the on-call doctor from the hospital group and informed her of the situation and apologized. No one likes to take care of an emergent failed home birth.

Then I had a glass of wine and tried to sleep, still feeling anxious and steaming. I finally fell into a fitful but deep sleep, and woke to my beeper going off at 6 o'clock the next morning with the number to the delivery room on the screen. I called back. One of the labor and delivery nurses answered, relaying the story of the previous night.

Here's what she told me: "About 2:00 in the morning, Ms. X was brought into Labor and Delivery by ambulance.

When the EMTs wheeled her into the delivery room, she was positioned on her hands and knees on the gurney, screaming. Meconium, the thick green fluid that signals fetal distress, was streaming down her legs. A nurse called the on-call obstetrician, Dr. G, who came in and took one look at the baby's heart rate on the fetal monitor."

Dr. G yelled, "Open the OR."

Dr. G thought they would need to do an immediate C-section. She then quickly examined the patient, and found the baby's head to be crowning, but Ms. X was still screaming and unable to push the baby out.

Dr. G said, "You have two choices. I can put a vacuum on the baby's head and pull, or we can do a C-section. Otherwise your baby may die."

Yes, she used that phrase: 'your baby may die.'

Ms. X agreed to the vacuum. After two pulls, the baby was out.

As angry and hurt as I had been feeling when I went to sleep, after hearing this story, my first feelings were sadness for Ms. X. She got exactly the delivery she didn't want: an emergency, an ambulance ride, a delivery by someone who had never met her, didn't know her, and had to pull her baby out. No birthing tub, no calm atmosphere in which to welcome her baby to the world, and certainly no pain relief. I imagined she was traumatized, and probably embarrassed.

I never heard from her again.

Recounting this story is hard because I return to that same hurt and anxiety. Colleagues and friends mostly reinforced my feelings of anger at being lied to and disrespected. My midwife colleagues had another perspective. They told me that this was not personal. They talked about the culture of general distrust of the medical profession, especially for pregnancy, labor, and delivery, and that this whole scenario was about the patient, not about me. They thought the patient saw withholding information as the only way to try to achieve what she wanted, excellent medical care I could offer, and then a non-medical, low intervention delivery in her own home. She would pretend she was going along with my plans but then follow the plans others were presenting. Those plans sounded more in line with the delivery she wanted—even if they were not following sound medical evidence. Ms. X had no way to compare these offerings of advice. She believed all held equal weight. She chose the pieces to follow because those were the ones she wanted to believe. Her choices almost cost her and her baby dearly.

Since that night, I have done my best to make my recommendations extremely clear to my pregnant patients. I encourage each one to engage in shared decision making with me about their labor and delivery plans, and what safe options exist for them. If we cannot agree, and may be heading for a similar Ms. X scenario, I strongly encourage them to be direct with me, and sometimes to seek care elsewhere. Sometimes they find care elsewhere. I don't feel hurt.

Thankfully, I have never been faced with a similar situation.

You Don't Always Get
What You Want

Ms. S came to see me for an annual exam and a consultation in my recently opened medical office. She was a healthy 34-year-old woman, married a little more than a year, and interested in becoming pregnant. This type of visit was one of my favorite consultations. My focus is preventative care, and the ideal time to assure a woman will have a healthy pregnancy is at a preconception visit. After an exam and Pap smear, Ms. S and I discussed diet, exercise, vitamins, immunizations, and family history, all important topics for a potential healthy pregnancy.

When we were done, I asked my usual question: "Is there anything else I can help you with today?"

Ms. S looked pensive and asked, "Yes, if I come to you for my pregnancy, and if I decide I want to deliver my baby by cesarean section instead of a vaginal delivery, would you do it?"

I thought for a moment. I had rarely come across this request before. Almost all my patients, especially those having their first baby, request, hope, and assume they will have a vaginal delivery. Women requesting a cesarean often had prior traumatic birth experiences, prior cesareans, or some type of poorly positioned baby late in pregnancy. Sometimes women had suffered from sexual or physical abuse, or had cultural or other aversions. These women could not bear to think about having a vaginal delivery, with the necessary vaginal exams or possible damage to their pelvic floor or vaginal tissues.

Ms. S did not seem to meet any of those criteria, nor had she mentioned this in the past hour during her exam and history discussion.

I said, "Usually there is some pressing reason women don't want to have a vaginal delivery. Is there something you can share with me about *why* you would choose a cesarean?"

She took just a moment, as if she knew I would ask her this question. "I just know myself. I just can't imagine a scenario where I would look forward to or enjoy the idea of something the size of a baby passing through an area the size of a walnut."

Ms. S seemed anxious to even be discussing this.

I quickly replied, "If that's what you decide, as long as I feel we've reviewed all the risks and benefits of that choice, of course I would."

She heaved a sigh of relief.

Only then did she tell me, "I've asked the same question of two other doctors. Both said 'no' because they did not agree with that decision."

I told her I valued a patient's autonomy to make her own choices, as long as I truly felt she was informed and understood all the possibilities. With that, Ms. S left, making an appointment to return in six months if she had not yet achieved a pregnancy.

Two months later, Ms. S was back in my office, newly pregnant, and excited but anxious. She was a physician's assistant in a local medical practice. People in the medical field sometimes worry more than others because they have more medical training and experience. They know firsthand how so many things can go wrong.

Ms. S had been taking my preconception advice: exercising regularly, following a healthy diet, and taking vitamins. She seemed on her way to a low-risk, healthy pregnancy.

When I performed her first ultrasound and saw a small worm-like structure moving around in its amniotic sac with a strong heartbeat, Ms. S and I shared a moment of pure jubilation. We established her likely due date, and began making plans for her prenatal visits. She reminded me of our earlier consultation, and her plans to have an elective cesarean when the time came. I assured her that I remembered. Since I was a solo practitioner, I was the only one that would be doing her visits and her delivery. She had no need to explain or defend her decision to anyone.

Ms. S's pregnancy progressed normally. She came for all her prenatal visits and followed all my advice. We came to know each other quite well. I met her husband, who was also excited but usually quiet during our visits. We discussed the details of her delivery, and I answered all her questions. I assured her that as we got closer to her due date, we would talk about every aspect of the delivery, as well as what to expect before, during, and after.

Toward the end of her second trimester, Ms. S went to the lab for a diabetes screening test. To her surprise, she was diagnosed with gestational diabetes, which is not like type 2 diabetes. Type 2 is usually the result of an unhealthy diet, not enough exercise, and genetics. Gestational diabetes can occur in a woman who is of normal weight and eating a healthy diet and exercising regularly. The placenta, which supplies the baby with blood flow and nutrition throughout pregnancy, sometimes makes it more difficult for the pregnant woman to utilize sugar in her bloodstream. This raises the blood sugar levels and creates gestational diabetes.

Ms. S was now considered a high-risk pregnancy. We needed to keep her blood sugar levels in the normal range. Once again, she followed all my advice. She monitored her sugar levels, educated herself about gestational diabetes, consulted with a dietitian, followed a low sugar diet, and exercised. She ultimately needed medication to manage her sugar, which was well controlled throughout the rest of her pregnancy. She and I discussed how that would be the best way to assure a healthy delivery and a healthy baby.

Ms. S began coming for weekly visits during her third trimester. At one of these visits we had a detailed conversation about what to expect on the day of her cesarean. I had scheduled the surgery for Thursday morning, in what was to be the week prior to her due date. When we schedule elective cesareans, we try to schedule within seven days of the due date to be as sure as we can that the baby's lungs will be mature enough to breathe outside the womb. Lungs are the last organs to fully develop in utero. Many women are delivered two or even more weeks prior to their due date, but if we were to plan the ideal time, we would schedule for the 39th week of gestation. We discussed when her last meal should be, what time to come to the hospital, and how events would go that morning.

Ms. S would be brought into the operating room. I would stay with her while she received a spinal anesthetic, so she could be awake during her cesarean. She would feel pressure but no pain. Her husband could be with her, but a screen would be placed so neither of them would actually see the baby being delivered. If the baby was fine, and if there were no complications (I reiterated to her: there could be heavy bleeding, infection, anesthesia complications, and several others), then she would be able to see the baby right away.

We discussed post-operative care, pain management, and the usual hospital stay of two to three days. I made sure Ms. S had my cell number, and at least one more appointment with me scheduled. I answered her remaining questions, had her sign an informed consent form, and reminded her to keep her sugars in excellent control until the delivery. We discussed how no one she might meet in the delivery room should try to dissuade her from her plan for an elective planned cesarean for her first baby. Not everyone agreed with this decision, but Ms. S was *MY* patient. She and I were in agreement. She left with a plan.

I have been an obstetrician long enough to know a **plan** is merely a suggestion of the best case scenario. Where pregnancies and deliveries are concerned, the universe often discards even the most carefully orchestrated plan.

A week before our scheduled cesarean date, my phone rang at 4:00 in the morning, waking me from my usual deep-but-not-too-deep sleep.

Ms. S, sounding breathless, said, "I think I'm in labor" between the breathing I had so frequently heard from so many women in various stages of labor.

I was immediately awake and coherent: "Go into the hospital. I'll meet you there."

I was worried something might be wrong. I went straight to the hospital wearing the scrubs I had been sleeping in. I called the delivery room to tell the nurses a patient of mine would be coming in.

"Ms. S is on her way. She is scheduled for an elective cesarean in a week, but she sounds like she is in labor."

I received the answer I was afraid I would get, "Well, if there's *no reason* for the section, maybe she can labor and have a vaginal delivery."

To which I replied, "She *does* have a reason, so please just open the OR and start getting her ready for a cesarean as soon as she gets there."

Ms. S and I had discussed this possible scenario. The choice was **hers**. She was not obligated to explain to anyone. This was her plan. Unless there was some other reason she was unable to have a cesarean right then, she should have what she wanted. Not all nurses would agree.

When I arrived, Ms. S was in a labor room, already changed into a hospital gown, with an IV running. She was huffing and puffing. I could see from her expressions and the monitor attached to her very pregnant belly that she was having strong regular contractions every five minutes. I said I would examine her so we knew how much time we had. I examined her cervix and found her to be four centimeters dilated, which was almost halfway to the size needed for a vaginal delivery.

I stood very close to her face and said gently, "You're approaching active labor. I know this wasn't your plan. It will take about 45 minutes to get everything ready for a cesarean, and during that time you will get more uncomfortable. I can give you pain medication through that IV, and we will move fast, as long as you still want to follow our plan."

If she had decided to do anything differently, this was the time for her to make it known.

She asked me, "What do *you* think I should do?"

I said, "I want you to do whatever *you* want."

Ms. S looked at her husband who was sitting quietly in the corner, looking more than a little nauseous. She then turned back to me.

"I want the cesarean." she said, deliberately.

I ordered pain medication, called in my assistant, and we moved toward the operating room.

Now feeling slightly more comfortable with the pain medication, Ms. S was able to walk into the OR with me. The OR team would be two delivery nurses and the anesthesiologist, Dr. A. He positioned Ms. S on the operating room table in order to place a spinal anesthetic. In spite of her inability to lie completely still, he expertly got the anesthetic in on the first try.

Ms. S immediately began to feel relief. Her entire demeanor changed, as she had been in severe pain for the last two hours. Her breathing slowed. She smiled as I helped one of the nurses roll her over onto her back so she could insert a catheter and wash off her abdomen with a surgical soap.

As soon as we started to roll her, Ms. S said, "I think I just peed on myself."

I said, "That may be your water breaking."

I looked under the sheet. A large amount of clear amniotic fluid was running down her legs and onto the OR table.

"The fluid is clear," I said. "That's good because clear means the baby is not in distress." I also told her, "I'm just going to check your cervix again since you won't feel it at all. I should know how dilated you are before we proceed."

When I re-examined her, I *had* to talk to Ms. S about a possible change in plans. Upon checking her cervix, I found her to be 10 centimeters dilated. The baby's head, with a full head of brown hair, was palpable and visible right at the vaginal opening. Ms. S didn't feel a thing. My eyes grew wide.

I moved up the table so I could be right up near her face: "To do a cesarean at this point would be more dangerous for the baby since I would have to push her head back up to do it. I believe you can push this baby out, but if you don't want to or can't, I can guide the baby out with a vacuum or forceps."

Ms. S looked at her husband. He was making a supreme effort to stay seated upright.

She turned back to me, and said "I trust you. Let's do this vaginally."

I sensed a collective sigh of relief from everyone in the room: three nurses, a surgical tech, Dr. A, and a nursing student. The baby was being monitored. Ms. S was completely comfortable. The pace slowed while we attached stirrups to the OR table and positioned her for a vaginal delivery. I told Ms. S to take a deep breath and push.

Fifteen minutes later, Ms. S gently pushed out a small baby girl, in a manner controlled enough to cause no damage to the vaginal or surrounding tissues. The baby immediately began crying. I placed her on her mother's belly. Everyone in the room cheered. Her husband was even able to stand and cut the umbilical cord. Ms. S looked at her baby with shock, awe, and a deep and immediate love. She and her husband were softly crying.

She looked at me and whispered, "Thank you so much."

After the placenta was delivered, and after I did my post-delivery clean-up, I left the room to do the orders and computer charting to go along with the delivery. Ms. S was wheeled to her postpartum room.

When I was done, I went to her room to again congratulate her and say goodbye. I was on my way to the office.

Ms. S said, "Thank you so much for always hearing me. I knew you were always on my side, and if you thought I could do it, then so did I. You know how I said I could never imagine a scenario where I could push a baby out of such a small space? Well, now I can."

I was wiping my eyes all the way to the office.

A Labor of Love and Pain

I had been an attending physician for about 10 years and was taking care of a patient, Ms. R. She was 30, pregnant with her first baby, athletic, and healthy. I had seen her for most of her prenatal visits, and my partners had seen her for the others. As usual, when we got toward the end of her pregnancy, we began to have conversations about what to expect during her labor and delivery. Ms. R, like so many other patients, heard lots of advice from family and friends who were advising on what they believed were the right things to do during her delivery. She listed these out for me:

- She wanted to go into labor on her own, no induction or medications.
- She wanted no pain medication during the entire labor process.
- She wanted to labor in a shower or tub, if possible.
- She wanted to avoid a cesarean delivery unless her life or the baby's life was in danger.

These are requests I often hear from patients, and, as was my usual habit, I wanted to discuss all these ideas with her. I asked what her thoughts were about medications, either for induction or pain management. Her answers were informed by ideas that others had presented to her as facts:

- Induction will make it more likely that you will have a cesarean.
- Pain medication, especially an epidural, will slow down your labor.
- Doctors do unnecessary cesareans all the time.

So much misinformation.

I was always willing to discuss each patient's desires for her ideal labor and delivery, but I believed we should have a conversation about why patients might have those desires, and whether their information is indeed in line with medical evidence. I wondered why a patient would come to me for the entire nine months of her pregnancy, trust me with her care, and follow most of my recommendations and directions. Then for the management of her delivery, she would choose to follow the direction of other people, sometimes *any* other people, instead of listening to what I would recommend. That was and is an unfortunate reality.

Ms. R and I continued our conversations about delivery. I explained that medical *evidence* showed the exact opposite of some of her information: that the best time for a baby to be delivered would be prior to or right around her due date. Continuing to wait past the due date, especially more than a week after the due date, which we had often done ten years before and when I was in training, significantly increased the chance that the baby would not tolerate labor, and she would be more likely to end up with a cesarean or a compromised baby.

Pain medication, given at the right time, including an epidural, does *not* slow down labor. In fact, medication some-times allows for relaxation and for the baby to descend into the pelvis. Sometimes pain medication moves labor along to the active labor phase and to delivery. And I certainly would never do a cesarean for 'no reason.' If Ms. R thought that of me, she may have been in the wrong office.

After a lengthy conversation, during which she seemed to understand my explanations, Ms. R said she would go home and discuss all this with her husband. She was 38 weeks pregnant at this point, and scheduled to return in a week.

When Ms. R returned the following week, she said she was willing to discuss things, but every discussion led back to the same place. She could not get it out of her head that taking medication was somehow bad, and that doing everything naturally was good. As long as the baby seemed safe and healthy, she believed nothing else was needed. She refused to discuss any plans other than her plan to 'wait for labor.' I would see her in the office weekly, and she decided we would deal with making plans for delivery when and if it became necessary. She had an appointment at 39 weeks, and again at 40 weeks. No labor. She was a bit swollen and quite uncomfortable.

Ms. R told me the baby was 'moving much less' at her 39 week appointment. When I told her that was alarming, she told me her sister had told her that was normal; her sister told her that the baby was 'running out of room, after all.' I advised her that this was not true; the baby should be just as active as he had been before if everything was okay, and if the placenta was still functioning normally.

As she was a day or so past her due date, I recommended she head to the hospital for a non-stress test (NST).

She debated this with me, declaring, "I know that once I go to the hospital, you won't want me to go home."

I replied that if something was worrisome on the monitoring that I was sending her for, of *course* I would not want her to go home. An NST was a 20 to 30 minute monitoring session of the baby's heart rate. We would watch the type of heart rate pattern the baby had. From this I could tell if the environment inside the uterus was still safe for the baby. If the placenta was not functioning well, or if the baby was not moving well, we should be able to see signs of that on the monitor. Ms. R, although reluctant, agreed to the monitoring session. She still worried that she was heading for the types of intervention she had so far refused, which she felt may be harmful to her baby.

Ms. R went to the hospital, and was hooked up to a monitor that would display her baby's heart rate and any contractions. She felt more uncomfortable than she had been in the office, and the monitor was registering a contraction every five minutes. The monitor displayed a normal fetal heart rate and rhythm, reassuring us that the baby was doing fine. As expected, Ms. R announced that she did not want to stay in the hospital for 'no reason.'

Even though she was feeling her contractions, she would go home and await more labor. I felt comfortable with this, as she and her baby were both stable. Ms. R could not see a reason to stay. After giving her guidelines on labor and fetal movement, I wrote her discharge papers along with a plan to follow up the next day in the office.

Our plans for the next day's appointment were unnecessary. As Ms. R stood up to go, we heard a soft popping sound.

I looked up at her face and saw her shocked expression. As the two nurses and I followed her gaze downward, we saw a large puddle of fluid accumulating on the floor and on and around her shoes.

I stated the obvious, "Looks like your water's broken."

Just as I was about to explain why I would now recommend even more strongly that she stay in the hospital, Ms. R's expression changed.

She grabbed her belly and let out a strong, loud moan, "OOOOOooooaaaaaaahhhhhh."

The moan went on for about 30 seconds. She held onto the triage bed that she had just gotten up from. Ms. R then took some slow deep breaths with her eyes closed. She didn't need convincing. When that contraction ended, the nurses quickly walked her down to a labor room. We began the admission process, setting up the room with everything she would need, putting orders into the computer, and filling out consent forms while explaining all the possible processes and procedures. In between these strong painful contractions Ms. R explained her plan, which we had discussed during her last few office visits:

- She wanted to labor in whatever position felt most comfortable (fine with me).
- She wanted to be as mobile as possible (fine with me as long as the baby was ok).
- She wanted no continuous IV fluids running (ok, as long as she allowed an IV access site, so in case of emergency we would have somewhere to give her medication).

- She wanted no medications to bring on stronger contractions (fine with me).
- She wanted no pain medication (that was totally up to her, and fine with me).
- She wanted limited exams (I totally agree with this, especially now that her water was broken).

These were all topics we had discussed before, and all were okay with me, as long as everything was okay with the baby.

Ms. R's husband then came into the room. He sat in a chair in the corner of her labor room. I explained all the things that were already happening, and asked if he had questions. He replied he did not. Even though Ms. R had stated she did not want exams, after about 15 minutes, she asked her nurse how we would know how close to delivery she was.

Nurse K replied "We don't, but if you feel like pushing, let us know."

Ms. R then asked if I would examine her just this once. She could then tell if her strong and painful contractions were moving her along toward her delivery, as she was in a lot of pain. I examined her between contractions and found her cervix to be three centimeters dilated, which was considered early labor. I asked if there was anything she wanted and if she had any questions before I went up to the charting area to do my documentation. She was extremely uncomfortable, but reiterated her desires for no medications and no interventions. I agreed that since everything seemed stable and reassuring we had no reason to change those plans.

After I finished her admission paperwork, I checked back in Ms. R's labor room. She was practically in tears, breathing and blowing through her contractions, rocking up and back on a large birthing ball. Her husband sat quietly in the corner. I thought this was strange. Usually when women in labor decided they did not want pain medication, their partner would be right next to them, or behind them, rubbing their back, or helping them breathe to cope in some way with the pain. Ms. R had been adamant. Her plan was no medication.

Before I left to go back to my office, I reminded her, "I will be very close by, just down the block. If you need me or if you get closer to delivery, I will be right back. Usually women having their first baby who are three centimeters dilated have six or seven hours to go, but since your water has already broken, maybe the delivery will be quicker. We have lots of things available to you, including a shower, a tub, various birthing balls and pillows for positioning, and of course, you can walk around in the room. Pain medication is always available if you decide you want any."

Her face was flushed and locked in a grimace. I wanted her to be aware that she had many options that could help alleviate her pain. All she had to do was ask. Ms. R reiterated her plan. I noticed that she looked at her husband after she repeated her plan for no medication. Her eyes looked a bit pleading as she turned toward him and then back to me.

He spoke up for the first time, addressing the nurse and me, "We'll be fine."

HE was clearly not in pain.

At this moment I had a thought that perhaps the plan for no pain medication and no interventions may not have been Ms. R's idea; maybe that was her husband's or someone else's idea. Unless she suggested any different, we would follow the birth plan she and I had discussed.

I rubbed Ms. R's back a bit, and said, "I am here to help you to go through this however *you* want to," hoping that she understood if *she* changed her mind I was there for her.

I went back to my office.

About two hours later, I got a call in the office: "Ms. R feels like she has to push," Nurse K said into the phone.

That was great news. I told the nurse I would be right there. As I speedily drove to the hospital from my office I thought how terrific it would be if Ms. R got exactly what she wanted: being fully dilated without pain medication, breathing through her contractions, and ready to push her baby out into the world.

When I walked into the labor and delivery suite, I heard loud rhythmic moaning, which I assumed to be my patient, getting closer to her delivery. I dropped my bag at the front desk and quickly washed my hands, entering her room with an excited smile. No one was in the bed. The loud moaning was coming from the bathroom.

Ms. R had one of the delivery rooms with a large tub and shower combination. She was laboring right where she had said she would want to, in the tub. The shower was running. She was in a crouched-over position, almost on her hands and knees, shower stream hitting her in the small of the back. Her husband was sitting on a stool outside the shower, and Nurse K was standing nearby trying to keep the fetal monitor at least intermittently applied to her belly, so we could hear the baby's heartbeat.

Ms. R was in the throes of active and transitional labor, not getting much of a break between her strong and frequent contractions. Tears were running down her face. She looked terrified. I asked if she felt like she had to push.

Between her contractions she said, "Sometimes."

She then reassumed her forward-bent position, rocking in the shower while the next contraction built up, peaked, and then slowly went away.

Between contractions, I asked, "Do you want me to check to see if you're ready to push? I can even check while you are still in the tub."

I had learned over the years how to check a woman's cervix in any number of positions they may be in: side-lying, standing, leaning, hand-and-knees. I grabbed a water-proof gown, and the nurse handed me the sterile gloves. We waited until the next contraction passed. I was able to maneuver myself around behind Ms. R and gently, if awkwardly, examine her cervix. She looked at me, hopefully.

I said, "You're really moving along!"

But I had to tell her the disappointing news that her cervix was six centimeters dilated, and only about 80 percent effaced. The numbers were not close to those needed to push a baby out. My heart always breaks to see a laboring woman in so much pain, but I am willing to assist her in going through her labor in whatever fashion *she* has decided to do so. In this case, however, I was not convinced that Ms. R was still on board with this plan.

Not wanting to be aggressive, but wanting to be her advocate, I said, "With a first baby, it's possible it can take another four or so hours until you are ready to push; or it *could* be sooner—no way to tell. If you feel the shower and breathing and moving are helping, you can certainly continue on. If you want to change course and get more comfortable, we can offer you various options; the door is open, and I can answer any questions you may have."

She was still moaning and breathing and rocking and crying, but she didn't say a word. She looked in her husband's direction. He was sitting on the stool, stoic. After a two minute pause, where the only sound was Ms. R's groans, I took my cue.

"OK, I'm going to go back to the office. If you need me, please call there." I said half to Nurse K and half to Ms. R and her husband.

I felt bad for my patient, but the decision was ultimately hers.

I went back to my office and tried to estimate how long before I would be called to come back to the hospital for the delivery. After so many years of obstetrical practice, the calculator in my head was always active. First baby.....6 centimeters.....one centimeter per hour, more or less. I guessed that in a few hours, Ms. R would feel that overwhelming sense of pressure, the signal that says to start pushing. I was looking forward to the start of the pressure. Thirty minutes later, Nurse K called my office.

"She is exhausted and crying and saying, 'I can't do this, I can't do this over and over.' I think you should come back."

I drove back to the hospital. When I returned to her labor room, Ms. R was curled up in a fetal position in the bed, crying.

She was repeating, over and over, "I caaan't do this....I caaan't do this!"

Her husband was still on that damn wooden stool in the corner. I thought this was strange. I went right over to the head of the bed, standing between her and her husband.

I leaned down and said, "I really think you **can** do this, if only you can get a little rest. You're exhausted, and the pushing phase is going to take all of your energy, probably for hours. Let's get you more comfortable."

I asked if it would be okay if I called the anesthesiologist, to give her an epidural, so she could get pain relief from the waist down. She would then be able to get some rest.

For the first time, she relayed the reason she had been so anti-epidural: "My husband doesn't want me to have one, but I *do* want it. I can't do this."

I called the anesthesiologist, who was down the hall in the on-call room, and explained the situation. Dr. M was there in the blink of an eye. I tried to advocate for my patient, and explain to her husband that relieving her pain would likely allow her to relax and have enough energy to push the baby out when the time came. He didn't say a word, but I thought he looked a little relieved.

I stayed with Ms. R throughout the insertion of the epidural. She leaned forward over the edge of the bed. I held her shoulders in a slouching position as Dr. M positioned her and found the right spot. Immediately after the test dose was placed, Ms. R's shoulders relaxed. Her breathing slowed. Her facial expression changed. She had relief. She laid back down on the bed, and I recommended she try to take a nap.

"No one will examine any more until you feel like pushing, or until we see some changes on the fetal monitor that tell us that you are ready to push."

Ms. R whispered "Thank you."

I squeezed her shoulder before I went back to my office. Mr. R said nothing. His shoulders and facial expression remained exactly the same.

"She is so strong," I said to him. "This is the most painful thing a woman can go through, and I want her to remember her delivery experience happily."

One corner of his mouth turned up. I assumed that was a smile. I went back to the office. I finished my office hours and went back to the delivery room. When I got to the front desk, I was able to see my patient's fetal heart rate tracing on the central monitoring system. The baby looked fine, but I could tell from the heart rate pattern on the monitor that the baby's head was very low and was likely getting gently compressed with each contraction. I smiled. I asked Nurse K to join me in Ms. R's room. She did.

The room was quiet when we walked in. Mr. R was in his usual spot, sitting on the stool in the corner. Ms. R was lying on her side, dozing comfortably.

I went over to the head of the bed, and whispered, "How are you feeling?"

"I'm not really feeling a thing."

I told her that I could tell from the pattern on the monitor she was getting very close to the time for pushing, and I would like to check her cervix to see if it indeed was time.

Nurse K helped Ms. R to roll over onto her back, as she did not have much feeling or control over her legs.

"This feels so weird," she said.

I put on my sterile gloves and examined: "Wow!" I said, "Your baby's head is *right there*." A full head of dark brown hair was visible and palpable, *right there*. "Let's have a baby!" I exclaimed, as I asked Nurse K to set the room up for a delivery while I ran off to the changing area to put on my scrubs.

When I got back to Ms. R's labor room, everything had been transformed. A delivery table and a lamp emerged from the large storage closet, and the labor bed was manipulated into the shape of a recliner with stirrups attached to the lower edge. Mr. R was still sitting, now on a stool next to the head of the bed. Ms. R looked relaxed but anxious.

I explained exactly how to push: "Take a deep breath like you're going underwater, then hold the breath and bear down, hard and long like you're pooping!"

After repeating these instructions several times, Ms. R was finally pushing effectively. We could see a little bit more of the baby's head with each push. The room was full of anticipation as we cheered Ms. R on with every contraction. After about fifteen minutes of long hard pushes, out popped the head, followed by shoulders and the rest of the long, chubby body. All of us—Nurse K, the nursery nurse, and even stoic Mr. R—cheered.

"Yay!" I said as I lifted the slippery baby boy and placed him, umbilical cord still attached, on Ms. R's bare belly.

For the first time in this whole ordeal, Ms. R's husband's face softened. I thought I saw a tear run down his cheek. They both looked lovingly at the baby. I knew they were feeling the surreal sensation that always took over in the first few moments after every delivery.

I removed the placenta and placed a few stitches, none of which seemed to bother Ms. R in the slightest. After I finished and cleaned up the area, I went to wash my hands and do all the delivery documentation. I was surprisingly exhausted considering the delivery itself had been fairly easy. I would be home early enough to have that salmon steak my husband was planning to broil.

I stopped back in Ms. R's labor room before I left. The couple were still cuddling and cooing over their new baby boy. Ms. R looked at me with what I could only recognize as satisfied exhaustion.

She said, "Thank you so much for all your help."

She was crying and exhausted and feeling no pain. I hugged her and told her and her husband I would see them in the morning.

The last thing I told her before I left was "When that epidural wears off, you will feel really sore, so please, *please* ask for pain medication if you need it."

I was about to explain which medications were available for her, but she cut me off.

She looked back at me with a sly, tired smile and said, "You don't have to talk to me about pain medication anymore. I get it. No reason to suffer, and they may even help me heal, and make my recovery better."

I smiled. Maybe Nurse K or Dr. M had had a conversation with her husband about managing a type of pain that he would never know.

Motherhood and Medicine, Part 3

In the fall of my last year of medical school rotations, my husband, son, and I went to a backyard birthday party for the child of a friend. I was six and a half months pregnant with my second baby. The party was a reminder of the whole world out there. People were doing all sorts of normal activities: going to movies and restaurants, raising children, and having vacations and backyard parties. I so enjoyed socializing with people not involved in medicine. The day was very warm, and my baby was moving a lot. I couldn't keep up with chasing after Jake, who was now two years old and always on the move.

I suddenly felt lower abdominal cramping. I knew from my experiences working in the prenatal clinic, and from all the books and information I had read, that dehydration can cause cramping in pregnancy and that some cramping, the Braxton-Hicks contractions, was normal. These are common cramps and contractions that occur as the uterus grows and the baby is active, but they do not come with any regularity or enough force to cause labor, or changes in the cervix. I hydrated and rested, sitting in a lawn chair under a tree. I tried not to be concerned, and did not want to worry anyone around me.

My pregnancy had been going perfectly: no complications, no abnormal test results. Growth was normal on ultrasounds. I had no reason to think anything was wrong. Besides, this was Sunday. I didn't think I needed to bother my doctor for something non emergent. When the cramping kept coming in spite of resting and hydrating all evening and into the night, I decided I would call Dr. L the next day.

Monday I went into the clinic where I was doing my rotation. When I got there, I called Dr. L's office. Nurse T came on the line. She told me to continue to hydrate, and come in later that day for a visit. During my stint in the clinic that day, I realized that I was contracting pretty regularly. Although I tried not to think about the contractions, I was surrounded by obstetricians and residents, as well as nurses, midwives, and physicians assistants, all of whom were used to seeing pregnant women in various stages of pregnancy with various complications. When three separate practitioners said I looked 'kind of uncomfortable,' I started to take note.

I left the clinic early, and went to Dr. L's office. He wasn't there, but his nurse practitioner saw me, did an exam, and took a urine sample. Nurse M told me to hydrate, and rest, possibly taking the next day off to stay home. She gave me a note to excuse my absence. I left the office feeling like, 'Well, if they didn't think this was such a big deal, I guess I shouldn't either.'

I was concerned but felt reassured. I stayed home the next day, waiting for Dr. L to call, to reassure me, and to say how worried-or-not-worried I should be. I wanted him to give me advice, or to at least talk to me.

At that moment, I made a large note-to-self about *my* eventual future obstetrical practice: I would never leave a worried patient hanging. I knew personally calling everyone every day to reassure them and answer questions would be unrealistic. Still, returning calls and reassuring patients, even if someone else was speaking on my behalf, should be doable.

I stayed home the next day, drank lots of water, rested, and worried. Every time I felt a cramp or contraction I worried. I waited to hear from Dr. L. He did not call. All day long. The next day I felt better, and went back to the clinic rotation. I was sure that whatever had been happening was only temporary. I told myself that all was well now. I worked and accomplished the usual tasks until Friday afternoon. Then I decided that my not getting a return call was strange. I decided to call his office.

Imagine my surprise when I asked about my urine culture and found out that I did have a urinary infection! Nurse M said that they would call a prescription into my pharmacy. She didn't sound at all concerned. As soon as I hung up, I made a decision. I felt worried. I felt anxious. I suddenly did not feel safe or low risk. I did not feel so well taken care of. Urinary tract infections can be dangerous in pregnancy. They can cause preterm labor, and they can cause problems for babies. And why did I have to call the office to get my results? I suddenly did not feel like my laid-back, low-risk doctor was right for me.

After agonizing for a few minutes, I boldly called the office of the high-risk perinatologists where I had done one of my fourth year rotations. I was practically crying on the phone, explaining that I was almost 29 weeks pregnant, and felt like 'something was not right.' I told them about the urine culture, the contractions, the perfunctory exam, and my fears. And kudos to them, Nurse C told me to come right in. I went there on that same day. That was obviously the end of their work day on a Friday before a three day weekend. Nurse C still said to 'come right in.' I remembered from my rotation with them. There were two partners, Dr. F and Dr. K, a woman and a man. They had shown such interest and compassion when treating and talking to their high risk patients. I knew I would be in good hands.

Dr. F did an ultrasound, a thorough exam, with other cultures, and told me that my cervix, although not open, was shortened. She was concerned that the contractions I had been feeling were preterm labor contractions. She was very reassuring, but told me that I would need to decrease my activity, stay well-hydrated, and do regular monitoring and exams to see if I would continue to be at risk for delivering early. I asked Dr. F if I could transfer my care to her practice, and deliver with her or one of her colleagues. She was kind and welcoming. I almost broke down realizing the catastrophe I might have just avoided. So much for my normal and low-risk pregnancy.

I returned to my clinic rotation, which was almost done by then. I told my supervisors that I would need to do shorter days, and perform many of my duties from a sitting position, with breaks in between for the bathroom and hydrating. They were accommodating, as I thought they should have been, given their specialty training and knowledge of potential preterm labor problems. I finished out the last week of the rotation continuing to learn, see, and treat patients while taking better care of myself and frequently seeing my new high-risk doctors. I made it to the early third trimester and had two more rotations to go. One was a mandatory lab rotation, where I was to work in a laboratory with a pathologist, looking at specimens from surgeons for identification and reporting.

Although my plan had never been to work in a specialty where I was not in direct contact with patients, I did feel the importance of knowing the non-patient side of lab tests, biopsies, and samples. Who is looking at these specimens and diagnosing conditions we clinicians were treating? What were they seeing? How did they know what diseases my patients had?

One of the perks of this rotation was the all-day-sitting and no-overnight-shifts, perfect timing for my pregnancy. Being in the lab was relaxing and calm. The work was interesting (sometimes) and boring (sometimes). I found pathologists and other lab workers an interesting bunch. The things that excited them were surprising and to me, strange. More than once, someone excitedly called me over to look at a bunch of cells under the microscope because they saw an exciting and unusual configuration, which led to some rare and interesting diagnosis.

I was buying time for my baby to grow and to think about my future. My last rotation was to end around Thanksgiving, and my baby was due on Christmas Day. I would hopefully have the last few weeks after being done with my fourth year rotations and medical school in general since I had already been to graduation, to really rest and get ready for the new baby. My preterm contractions seemed to have gotten under control, with resting and hydrating. I was now also going for weekly monitoring sessions to check on the baby's well-being and for regular contraction patterns that I might have not been aware of. My last rotation would truly be a test to see if I could make it through without my baby making an early appearance.

At my 36 week prenatal visit, Dr. F checked the position of the baby, head down and ready. She also checked and said that since the last time I delivered I was so advanced in labor before even getting to the hospital, this time I should not wait until the contractions were very, very strong, or even very regular. I should call and go into the hospital when I was feeling something different, a sensation of pressure, or unusual aches and pains, even if I was just worried. This was all so I would have a chance to calmly get to the hospital before I was in advanced active labor.

My last rotation, endocrinology, was a clinic rotation with regular hours and lots of days off. The rotation ended just as I completed my 37th week of pregnancy. I was excited to be done with medical school. I had only my family to share my excitement with. I was unceremoniously *done*, had already gone through the graduation rite-of-passage, and would not be starting a residency until the following July.

I was starting to think about applying for residency spots, when at 37 weeks and one day, I was trying to fall asleep, without much success. I suddenly realized I *WAS* feeling different. I felt a lot of downward pressure and achiness. I thought I should head over to Labor and Delivery to at least get checked even though the digital clock said 2:00 in the morning. I called Dr. F, who said to definitely go in. I then called my mom, who was ready to stay with Jake.

My husband and I drove to the hospital, which was about 20 minutes away. I got progressively more uncomfortable as we traveled. When we got there and checked in, I was uncomfortable but not tremendously so. Dr. F came in and checked me. She told me I would be admitted since I was six centimeters dilated. This is considered active labor. Based on my past experience, that meant that I would soon be having the baby.

I was admitted, changed into a hospital gown, and had some labs drawn. The process seemed very undramatic. I was not uncomfortable, but excited with anticipation. I was laboring and breathing through my contractions. The nurse came in to see how I was doing. I told her I was okay so far, but I must have looked pretty uncomfortable because she suddenly appeared with a syringe of Demerol, which is a narcotic pain medication. She asked if I wanted her to inject the Demerol into my IV. I was not much of a pain-medicine-user. Although labor pain would truly soon become 'other dimension' pain, I asked if she would divide the dose, and give me half first. If I needed the other half, I could get it later.

She was fine with that and proceeded to inject 12.5 mg of Demerol into the IV. This is considered a pretty small dose, but I thought that would be enough to dull the pain. The nurse had just started to inject the dose into my IV, but before she even pushed in the total half dose, before I felt any relief, I felt something else.

I said, "I need to push," and I did.

She called Dr. F in, and four or so contractions later, at 5:38 that morning, Danielle came squealing out into the world, tiny but perfect. I thought only of the line in the Grinch movie, where my heart 'grew three sizes that day.'

In the last nine months of my pregnancy I had been living with a certain low-level fear. I knew how overwhelmingly and immediately I loved my first born, Jake, from the moment he was born. During my second pregnancy, I was quietly anxious that I would not have as much love in my heart for another baby, or at least not enough. I never expressed this fear out loud, but I wondered how the amount of love needed to take care of a newborn could multiply exponentially.

The moment I delivered all my fears about not having enough love for another child went away. I still wasn't sure about having enough *energy* for another child, but I wasn't thinking about that at the moment. When I looked at my tiny wrinkly baby girl, I didn't think about medicine, or travel, or exams, or residency applications. I only thought how thrilled I was, and how lucky to have this new, perfect baby right there, in front of me, on me, and next to me. After all I had seen, in high-risk obstetrics, in NICUs, and in perinatal clinics, all the complications and potential bad outcomes, and all I had been doing to avoid them, I was overwhelmingly happy. And so lucky. And I was definitely and absolutely in love, again.

Painful Insertion

Ms. M came into my office on one warm spring day. She was a new patient, 32-years-old, and interested in discussing birth control options. I had been providing birth control education, information, and devices to women for many years.

The conversation usually started by asking patients, "Are you the type of person who is fine with thinking about your contraceptive method every single day, the type of person that never wants to think about it at all, or somewhere in between?"

I ask this question because the answer will then set me on the path to begin my consultation with the methods that may seem most appealing and appropriate for each patient.

Ms. M said, "I would love to have something that I really don't have to think about for a long time, set it and forget it."

One of my favorite long acting reversible contraceptive methods is the intrauterine device. The IUD is a contraceptive that is inserted into the uterus in an office visit, and is effective for a long period of time, three, five, or ten years, depending on which device, for pregnancy prevention. I took out my pamphlets and educational materials, only to have Ms. M hold up her hand before I started talking.

"Nope" she said, "Not an IUD. I have too many friends who have told me about their horrible experiences with an IUD, and I am **not** going there."

I asked her to elaborate. All she was able to say, and repeat, was that she had heard having an IUD placed was one of the worst experiences of her friends' lives, that 'no one had told them it was going to be so bad,' and that weeks or months later her friends were still uncomfortable. She did not have any exact details of her friends' experiences. I decided I might want to take a closer look at exactly *how* women were getting these devices placed, and *why* some health care providers and clinics may not be doing everything they could to make the experience less traumatic and less uncomfortable for their patients.

While no method is 100 percent sure for contraception other than abstinence, the IUD has about a 97 to 98 percent pregnancy prevention rate. It does not rely on remembering to take or use anything and is not affected by the calendar or the timing of a menstrual cycle. It does not depend on how responsible either partner is about using it correctly. This certainly fits the criteria for a 'set it-and-forget it' method, as IUDs can remain in place for years.

Even when the girl/teen/woman is in the office to speak specifically about her desire for or her fear of an IUD, we first review the details of how all methods of birth control work and the risks and benefits of each. Then we get more specific, discussing various IUDs, what she can expect after IUD insertion, and what the effect on her menstrual cycle may be. We discuss any current and future childbearing plans, and any history of infections, pregnancies, medical problems, surgeries, and past use of contraception. After this conversation, if the IUD seems the method of choice, and if she seems a good candidate, we go on to do an exam.

I can do a Pap smear during the exam if the patient is due for one, and collect cultures to make sure she has no current vaginal infection. According to the Center for Disease Control guidelines, an infection should not preclude an IUD insertion. However, common sense tells me that if a patient has a current vaginal infection, especially a sexually transmitted one, I would prefer to treat the infection before I place a device into the uterus.

I can also feel the size and shape of the uterus during the exam. I check to determine if the uterus feels big enough for an IUD. The size of a uterus does not guarantee if that will be the case just from an exam, but I have sometimes felt that a uterus is too small, too irregularly shaped, or is abnormal in some way. All of these would possibly necessitate a change in the way I may be planning to place the IUD, or which one to place. Some IUDs are smaller than others.

Further evaluation may be necessary before the day of insertion. Most importantly, I could look at the cervix, and would be able to tell if it would allow an IUD to be inserted without much difficulty. If the patient had a vaginal delivery within the last few years, the cervix will probably do just fine. If the patient has never had a baby, or had only cesareans, her cervix may need some help to open enough for the insertion.

Ms. M was unsure whether any of this had been done at the exams preceding her friends' IUD experiences. She seemed to be softening a little to the idea that her experience in my office may not be the same as her friends' experiences.

After that initial exam, we talk about plans: Of course, not everything on my list is possible for all women, but knowing that these options exist may make the experience less unpleasant if the options are available and discussed.

1. Choice of IUD

The first step is deciding which IUD to insert. A copper IUD is just for contraception, and should not, after the first few months, affect the menstrual cycle. Periods may be heavier at first, but should return to a pattern similar to pre-IUD menstruation. The same applies to cramping. A progesterone-releasing IUD, and at last count at least four different ones are available in the US, provides contraception and will also have some effect on the menstrual cycle. Different progesterone-containing IUDs have different effects; some are designed to eliminate the period altogether, and some will create shorter, lighter periods. Eliminating the period with the IUD is a desired benefit for many women, and confers no known risk to future fertility. Some progesterone IUDs are known to cause irregular spotting or bleeding. The best is knowing what to expect depending on which IUD will be placed. Some progesterone-containing IUDs have been known to be responsible for various other side effects: acne, mood changes, and bloating. Unfortunately, we do not know if anyone will suffer these side effects until the IUD is placed. Some women cannot tolerate their side effects and will choose to have the IUD removed after a short period of time. In my experience, this is a small number of women.

2. When to schedule

I recommend that a patient come in to have the IUD inserted while having her period. Sounds messy, I know, but we see bleeding all the time, and would rather have a cervix that's a bit open because of the current active bleeding. The cervix will be softer, and will make insertion somewhat easier if done during a period. Also, as a secondary reason, having a period usually, but not always, assures us that there is no current pregnancy at the time of the IUD insertion. We will, of course, do a pregnancy test prior to insertion, but currently bleeding with a period, especially if the period came at the expected time, is reassuring.

3. Pain medication

I recommend taking some strong pain medication prior to the insertion. I am often shocked to hear that patients have not been advised to take *anything* prior to the procedure. That doesn't make sense. The medication may not be a narcotic, although I have been known to prescribe one or two pills of Vicodin if someone other than the patient is driving home. If on exam, the cervix is tightly closed, or seems the insertion may be difficult, something strong may be necessary! Even if inserting an IUD doesn't seem difficult, having instruments attached to, and inserted into the uterus is *not* a walk in the park! Ibuprofen is one option, but many other pain medications and anti-inflammatories can be used to lessen the discomfort of the insertion process.

Ms. M did not know if any of her friends had been offered or had taken any pain medicine before their insertions.

4. Other Medication

Misoprostol is a medication that can be taken the night before the IUD insertion and will usually soften and help open the cervix. Occasionally, this medication has been the difference between my being able to place an IUD, and having to recommend another method of contraception. Misoprostol is used to induce labor. This medication has some possible side effects and should be taken with food. Side effects are mostly cramps and bleeding, to which I tell my patients, "Perfect, it's working!" Chemically softening the cervix with medicine prior to insertion has truly changed my ability to more gently place IUDs, with less trauma to the cervix and to the patient!

Ms. M was fairly certain she had never heard of this medication.

5. Written instructions

Good written instructions on what to do and what to expect for the hours and days following the procedure are crucial. Discussions are easily forgotten, especially if a woman is apprehensive about the insertion, and after-pains can be scary. The instructions should explain what to do if a fever, severe pain, or unusual bleeding arises. Some serious complications could happen in the immediate post-insertion time period. Having a written plan to refer to can also go a long way toward easing anxiety that may be associated with the entire process.

Once we finished reviewing all this information, I answered Ms. M's questions about the various types of IUDs as well as other methods of long-acting reversible contraception. She had a change of heart. We successfully placed her first intrauterine device the following Thursday.

After I placed it, I told her, "The IUD is a wonderful way for women to take control of their reproductive decisions. The process of acquiring one should not have to be traumatic, painful, and anxiety-ridden. I'm glad we were able to lessen that anxiety, and the discomfort associated with the actual procedure. I hope that this particular procedure will never be described as the 'worst experience of your life.' There are lots of other events that may earn *that* title."

Ms. M reminded me of this very conversation when it was time for the IUD to come out five years later. She was thinking about having a baby.

I responded, "Let me tell you my thoughts on pain-free childbirth…."

It Works!

One morning I was working in my office, seeing my usual schedule of patients when I received a message from one of my receptionists.

"Dr. Katz would like you to call her."

I didn't recognize the name, but that wasn't unusual since we lived in an area with so many hospitals and doctors. Unless I had direct interaction with a particular doctor, I may have never been aware of her. The message didn't mention a particular patient or ask a specific question. I was curious. I called the number back at the end of my office hours, and had a twenty or so minute conversation with Dr. Katz.

"Hello," I said when she picked up the phone on the second ring. "This is Dr. Levy, and I got a message to give you a call back. I'm sorry, I don't think we've met."

Dr. Katz was a physical therapist and doctor of clinical sexology. Her partner, Dr. Tabisel, was a sex therapist, licensed social worker, and a doctor of clinical sexology. They owned the Women's Therapy Center, which was not too far from my office. They were dedicated to treating women with certain difficult genital, sexual, and emotional conditions. The office had been open for the past few years, although both practitioners had been in business elsewhere for many more years. Dr. Katz explained a little about what they did in their practice. I was intrigued. She invited me to come to their office and discuss ways we might collaborate to help the women under their care. Their approach sounded unique for conditions that were difficult to treat in the general medical or gynecological office. I eagerly accepted her offer to visit and talk further.

The following Wednesday afternoon I approached the main entryway doors at the Women's Therapy Center. I entered the first large glass door and was met by a small alcove with a locked door and a buzzer system with an intercom. This was a little unusual. Most medical offices had freely-opening front doors that patients and others could easily access. I wondered about the reason they needed to verify identities prior to allowing access to their office.

Once I identified myself a muffled voice said, "Just a minute."

At least, I thought that's what the voice said. A loud buzzer sounded, signaling me to push on the glass door and enter. I passed through the door and found myself in a small, quiet, comfortable waiting room, alone with six cushioned chairs.

A whiff of lavender wafted through the air. Asparagus ferns and spider plants ringed the room. Lots of books and magazines were on the tables. I sat down. My eye caught on a book that looked like a home-made photo album. Flipping through the pages, I began to get a sense of the activity in the Women's Therapy Center. The album was full of letters and photos from patients, with the actual names blacked out. One letter after the other was *full* of accolades, praise, and declarations from patients about their 'lives being saved' and their 'marriages being saved' by whatever it was that they were doing here at the Women's Therapy Center, with Dr. Katz and Dr. Tabisel.

I was more intrigued. By now I had been in practice long enough to have gotten my share of letters from grateful patients. Delivering their babies or diagnosing and treating a patient's condition was reason enough for many patients to write thoughtful thank you notes, but never had I gotten such heartfelt and extreme letters such as those in this photo album. Whatever they were doing here, I wanted to be a part of it.

After a few minutes, a young woman came out into the waiting area and greeted me warmly.

"Hi Dr. Levy. Let me show you around."

I stood and she led me through another door with another intercom and down a hallway with four rooms, each with a closed door, two on each side of the hallway. The hallway was quiet, and the air still had the lavender scent. The woman led me to a room at the end of the hall.

She opened the door to a large conference room where two women were seated at a huge table. Several plates on the table had healthy snack foods: crackers and veggies and dip; slices of apples and mangos; and bottles of water. I wasn't expecting a meeting with snacks!

Dr. Katz was a serious looking Israeli woman with short blonde-gray hair and wire-rimmed glasses. She stood, held out her hand, and shook mine firmly.

"Hello. Great to meet you! We've heard about you from some of our patients and colleagues, and we have a proposal for you. I thought we would tell you about what we do here, and then get to the working relationship."

Dr. Tabisel, who had been sitting quietly, then shook my hand as well. I realized when she stood up to greet me that she was petite and athletic looking. She smiled broadly, and I sat down.

They told me what I came to hear: The Women's Therapy Center had been established in 1996 with a goal of addressing women's physical and emotional needs in a holistic manner. They had created unique programs for women who were suffering from painful sexual conditions, like dyspareunia (painful intercourse), vaginismus (painful muscle spasms of the pelvic floor), and vulvodynia (painful genital conditions with burning or throbbing nerve pain). They treated women from all over the world who came to spend time at their center and be treated and cured of these complex gynecological conditions. They had written a book, *Private Pain*, had participated in research, and had done numerous speaking engagements on these and other topics.

My question to myself was why had I not met these two women before? These very conditions were some of the most complicated and difficult I had been encountering as a gynecologist. These women had been successfully treating them for years!

During their presentation, I wondered why they needed me.

They went on to tell me something I already knew: neither of these amazing practitioners was a physician. They were not gynecologists, even though they were dealing, quite effectively, with problems that were very much in the realm of the gynecologist. Because they weren't gynecologists, they could not do some of the things their patients needed: They could not prescribe medications, they could not do Pap smears or biopsies or diagnose certain conditions that were out of their scope of practice. They wanted to provide *complete* care to their patients: that was where I came in.

"Sometimes," they told me, "we have a patient who just cannot undergo this type of treatment without anti-anxiety medication. And sometimes, we are in the process of treating a patient for their pain syndrome, and we see something that requires an exam by a gynecologist, a biopsy, or a diagnosis, and *we* cannot do that."

They were asking me to be a consulting physician and to be available to participate in these treatment plans if and when they needed me. I was intrigued but still wanted to know more about the treatments they were so successfully performing on their patients who had conditions that were some of the most difficult to solve in my 'regular' gynecology practice.

Turned out that these two women had developed a proprietary and trademarked detailed treatment protocol that included the physical, emotional, psychological, and spiritual aspects of therapy. They had 'expert interventions with a focus on the inseparable association between a woman's body and her mind' (womentc.com). They didn't give me all the details, noting that physicians who are looking to implement their exact treatment plan pay them for the information. They did explain the basics of their plan. When they finished, I was amazed by the sense and simplicity of their plan and their success rates. They saw women of all ages and in all life situations, women who suffered from a variety of usually painful and often embarrassing conditions. After several short weeks of therapy sessions, these problems seemed to be completely solved. I saw the letters of testimony to prove their work.

I wanted to be a part of this.

For the next five years, I often went to their office. I examined patients, made suggestions, did Pap smears and biopsies, prescribed medications, and had many wonderful conversations with the owners, the staff, and the patients. I met many patients who entered treatment sad and hopeless, only to leave hopeful and renewed. They became educated and empowered and ready to take control of their bodies and their relationships.

I came to believe that the conditions being treated at this amazing place were never something that could be taken care of with a single method: the conditions needed a combination of treatment approaches, where the physical, psychological, and emotional needs of each patient were considered. I have had much success with this approach and have Drs. Katz and Tabisel to thank for the many women with these same devastating conditions that I have helped in my own practice.

I was thinking about them and their approach when a patient came to see me about four months ago. Ms. J was young: 54 years old. She relayed a sad but not uncommon story to me. At age 45, she had been diagnosed with breast cancer. She needed a mastectomy and then chemotherapy. For several years, her life had been focused on treatment and survival. She was married and felt her husband had been very loving and supportive during her medical ordeal.

The physical relationship with her husband and all sexual intimacy had been put on the back burner as she went through the various stages of her cancer treatment. She was teary eyed when she told me her story, especially when she relayed the problem that landed her in my office. She and her husband had not had intercourse for eight years. Any time they tried, she had so much pain and so much anxiety that they abandoned the idea. They didn't talk about what was happening, and more time would pass. Ms. J now felt she might be losing her loving, supportive husband.

As had often happened in these consultations, I tried to be reassuring when I said to this patient, "I have a *special* treatment plan for you, and I was coached by the creators of the method."

As I had so many times in the years since I left New York and my consultant position at the Women's Therapy Center, I explained my plan. Ms. J was somewhat skeptical but reluctantly agreed to try.

Eight weeks later Ms. J sent me a postcard from Hawaii with two words written on it: "It worked!"

The Laser Is Going Where?

When I started my second year of private practice in California, I was trying to decide my focus. I had always been a general Ob/Gyn. In my last few years in practice, I began to focus more on women in the perimenopausal and menopausal age bracket. Many local Ob/Gyns cared for women who needed birth control, who had infections, and who wanted to have babies. Women over age 40 didn't have a particular place where their gynecological problems could be addressed by an expert in the field. I started going to conferences and medical meetings, and learning all I could about the special problems that women over 40 had.

The list included bladder leakage, irregular period issues, menopausal symptoms like hot flashes and insomnia, osteoporosis, and weight gain. One particular problem was frequently mentioned: vaginal dryness and discomfort, leading to painful sexual encounters. This was a complaint I saw daily. I wasn't sure if more women were suddenly realizing they had this problem, or if I was asking more questions, but many more women were describing this. Other doctors had not yet offered a satisfactory solution. I decided to make treating vaginal dryness an important part of my specialty, to always discuss it with my patients, and to offer solutions.

The medical term for the constellation of complaints that includes vaginal dryness and painful intercourse is genito-urinary syndrome of menopause (GSM). Many women do not mention their symptoms to their doctors or health care practitioners, feeling that GSM is a normal or expected part of aging. Many health care providers do not inquire about these symptoms due to lack of time or knowledge, or because of embarrassment. They may believe that if the patient does not bring it up, then GSM is not an issue.

The reality is that so many women are dealing with GSM and not just menopausal women. Postpartum women, women on certain forms of birth control, women who are breastfeeding, and women who have survived cancer, especially breast cancer have something in common. These are conditions for which the body lacks estrogen, which is responsible for keeping vaginal and vulvar tissues moist, elastic, and pain free. When a woman does not have estrogen, or cannot use estrogen, she may suffer from all the symptoms of GSM.

The cornerstone of treatment for these conditions has been to replace the estrogen, or use an estrogen-like medication, and the symptoms would likely disappear. I became knowledgeable about all the prescription and non-prescription methods that women could use to try to replicate the effects of estrogen on their vaginal tissues to get relief from their painful and sometimes severe symptoms. I often gave patients lists, samples, and articles about the products created so they could make choices and effectively treat their pain and dryness, and return to the type of comfort and intimacy they were missing.

Medical device and pharmaceutical companies closely track the prescribing habits of physicians. These companies have access to lists that the pharmacies compile about which physicians prescribe which medications. This is how the companies learn who to target for sales pitches, visits to offices, and discussions. As I was using many of the available medications on my now increasing patient population, I was not surprised when I received a phone call and then an office visit from a sales rep. She represented a company making and marketing a vaginal laser device, which was designed to address the very problem I was so frequently treating.

At first, and for the first few months that she called and knocked at my door, I would not respond. Nor would I see her. I had never heard of this device, except in passing at medical conferences. My mind immediately went into skeptic mode: 'This is a gimmick; she is trying to sell an expensive piece of equipment.' I was too busy to entertain the idea of learning about this new device and procedure, and too broke to buy an expensive laser device, having just fully furnished and stocked my new office.

She persisted. My receptionist took her numerous messages. I didn't respond. One night as I was leaving my office, she showed up at my door. I could not avoid her as I was walking out. She said one sentence when she saw me practically roll my eyes at her.

"Just look at the studies."

She handed me a stack of studies on the vaginal CO_2 laser device and surveys of patient outcomes. The stack had lists of patient names, patients who had the procedure and were willing to talk about it. Then she was gone. The stack sat next to me when I drove home that night. The next morning I brought it to my office.

The studies, surveys, and lists occupied the left corner of my desk for a week before I got around to looking at them. I slowly read the history of the device and the inventors in Italy. I had been pretty successful in treating my patients who had been complaining about these painful conditions, but I had recently been feeling frustrated about my patients who could not, or would not, use any vaginal estrogen products. Some women could not use estrogen because they had histories of breast or uterine cancer; others would not use it because they were afraid to use hormones of any kind. Not much was helping them. No lubricants, moisturizers, and recipes for products without estrogen were helping them to have comfortable sex with their partners. The patients and I were getting discouraged.

I called Ms. B, one of the women close to the top of the list.

She said, "After I had chemo, I was too busy worrying about surviving to think about my sex life. But when I was ready again, I just could not! Only this laser got me back to my physical relationship with my husband."

Her remarks intrigued me. I called twelve other women, and ended up spending hours hearing their experiences about the CO_2 vaginal laser procedure. Their testimonials were amazing and convincing. I kept hearing that after treatments with this laser device, these women had returned to having comfortable, pain-free sex with their partners, after not being able to enjoy sex for weeks, months, or even years. Not every woman was 100 percent satisfied. I'd have been suspicious if they had been, but I listened to enough stories from enough patients to think that this treatment may be worth investigating.

Over the next three months I traveled to several doctors' offices that offered the laser treatment to see what it entailed, and to learn how they had set up their offices for this procedure. I attended specialty conferences where this laser technology was explained. I flew to Los Angeles where I was surprised to be in a large auditorium with over 100 doctors from all over the country. A panel of doctors, physicists who were laser specialists, and marketing reps gave animated presentations on every aspect of this technology and how it could be incorporated into all of our practices. Physicians at the forefront of menopause management, sexuality, and cancer treatments spoke about the success they had in their patient populations.

I felt like I was opening up a new and unexplored world, an unknown territory. I read about the company, the origins, the founders, and the studies conducted on the use of the CO_2 laser. I learned about the risks and benefits. I was intrigued, and more than excited when I got home.

I then surveyed my own patients about whether this treatment would be something they would consider if I decided to offer it in my practice. I handed out my own articles and surveys to see if there was interest. One big problem was doing a procedure in my office that would treat a painful medical condition but was not eligible for insurance coverage. I understood that laser *cosmetic* procedures would not be covered, but this procedure was not cosmetic. The goal is not to make the vagina or the vulva more visually pleasing. It was not designed to rejuvenate or tighten the vagina. This is a medical procedure designed to treat a constellation of medical conditions: dryness, pain, frequent urinary tract infections, and discomfort during sex.

I could not wrap my head around charging money for this procedure, which possibly would not be reimbursed for patients. I thought about the things for male sexual pleasure that are covered all the time!

After my research and self-education, I bit the bullet and bought the machine. I have now been treating patients for over three years, and it is one of the most satisfying options I offer. I have treated women who had not been able to have sex for years. I have treated women who could not sleep because they were so itchy in the genital area. I have treated patients with bladder issues and dryness, pain from a non-healing tear after a traumatic vaginal delivery, and women who report constant burning and pain in the genital area. I have treated women from ages 32 to 92. Almost all of them have gotten better. Almost all of them have gotten relief. I *know* that this is the only treatment out there that could have done it.

I definitely do not treat every woman who comes in asking for this procedure. Not all women are candidates. I have had women come in and ask me to do this procedure to 'make their vagina young again' or to 'tighten it up.' I have had to tell them that this is not the procedure for them. The $CO2$ laser is not a rejuvenator. The laser is a medical procedure that is a relief-provider and often a relationship-saver.

A patient, Ms. G, recently went through the series of laser procedures. She had complained to me of her inability to have sex with her husband after her treatments for breast cancer. They were struggling. After 10 years of being unable to be intimate with her very loving partner, they were once again able to get back to a physically intimate relationship after three laser treatments to the vagina. She was satisfied. He was satisfied. Her husband gave me one of my best online reviews.

Now that's satisfaction.

Motherhood and Medicine, Part 4

My second year as an employee in a private practice in New York was turbulent. I had two children under the age of ten, my marriage had ended, and I was trying to find a healthy work-life balance. Being a full time physician and a full time single mother often left me feeling like I was doing neither of those jobs well enough. I had to be away overnight at least twice a week, and the various baby-sitters and nannies that I hired never seemed to work out for the long term.

I also attended conferences related to my work since I had to keep up with advances in the world of women's health. One of the conferences was in San Francisco, and as it was my ex-husband's vacation time with our kids, I took the opportunity to attend. At that conference I met the man who would become my new husband. We were friends first, and the friendship grew into love and commitment. We started a new life together, planning for the future, including the possibility of having our own baby. I wanted more children, but I was already over 35, elderly by pregnancy standards.

When I became pregnant, I was reluctant to reveal the pregnancy to my bosses and coworkers, as I was the newest hire. As the familiar tiredness of early pregnancy set in, I tried to keep up with my busy office and on-call schedule. Life wasn't easy. After hiring baby-sitters who did not want to stay overnight, I was lucky to find a wonderful nanny to live with us on a part-time basis.

T was from Trinidad. She lived in Brooklyn and was great at shuttling my kids to their various activities. She was tall, with closely cropped hair and a lilting voice. She spoke Trini English, deleting words from sentences and speaking exceedingly fast, but the kids understood her well enough. T stayed overnight on the nights I was on-call, so she would be there if I got called away. Her being there was a huge relief and lowered the anxiety I had faced about leaving home in the middle of the night.

A few days before Christmas I was deeply sleeping when my phone rang at 2:00 in the morning. When I answered, my boss said he needed me to come to the hospital to assist in an urgent cesarean for a patient in preterm labor with twins. I dragged myself out of bed, left a note for T, and made my way out to my car, travel coffee mug in hand. Fifteen minutes later I was in the hospital delivery room, wide awake, focused, and changing into my scrubs. I glanced at the patient's chart but didn't recognize her name.

Ms. C was already in the OR. The anesthesiologist was placing her spinal anesthesia. I peeked into the waiting area and was surprised to see Mr. C, the expectant husband. I recognized him from the nearby hospital where I had finished my residency six years earlier. He was the talented ultrasound technician I had come to know well over my four residency years. Ultrasounds are ordered so often in obstetrics and gynecology that our paths had crossed multiple times. We had become friendly, having had many late-night conversations about hospital procedures and gossip, New York politics, and where to get the best Mexican food on Long Island.

"Wow, those are *your* twins in there?" I asked him.

He looked nervous but seemed happy to see me and relayed some of the details of his wife's pregnancy: She had been coming to our practice for the entire pregnancy, but mostly had seen the other doctors for her prenatal care. A day earlier she started having preterm contractions and was admitted to the hospital. She was pregnant with twins, and the lower twin was breech (butt down), which would require a cesarean for delivery. In the middle of the night her water had broken. That meant the cesarean had to be done as soon as possible. She was 37 weeks pregnant, a bit early.

Just then, I was called to the OR over the intercom. We were ready to begin. I said hello to Ms. C, and realized I actually had seen her once in the office, but hadn't made the connection. Her husband was escorted in, and took the seat right by her head. The cesarean was fairly uneventful. Both the girl and the boy came out crying. In spite of the late hour, the OR was buzzing with the excitement that always accompanied a twin birth, with double everything in the OR: two nurses, two cribs, two pediatricians, and twice as much equipment.

When the adrenaline of the moment had worn off, I realized my early-pregnant self was exhausted. My back was hurting. I changed and went to the recovery area to say congratulations and goodbye. I shared my secret with Mr. and Ms. C.

"Sorry I'm so out of it," I whispered, "But I'm pregnant!"

I felt so good to reveal the pregnancy since I hadn't yet told many people.

I got home with just enough time to shower while T prepared breakfast for my kids. I drove them to school on my way to the office, functional but exhausted.

"I need to tell everyone really soon," I told myself as I pulled into the parking lot.

This wouldn't be a secret for long.

⌒

Fast forward five years, and I was standing in line to enroll my now five-year-old son, Dylan, in a Montessori preschool program in my neighborhood. I felt a tap on my shoulder. I turned around, and saw Ms. C with five year old twins, a girl and a boy, each clinging to an outstretched hand. The twins couldn't have looked more different; the girl was taller, and wore glasses; the boy was shy and hid behind his mom. I hadn't seen Ms. C since the night of the twins' delivery. We introduced our children to each other.

After some small talk, she said, "I have never forgotten that you came in, exhausted and pregnant in the middle of the night to assist in my cesarean. Thank you."

I smiled at the comment and the now-distant memory.

⌒

Fifteen years later, my son and the twins are still friends. At the crossroads of motherhood and medicine is a small, strange world.

Third Year Student,
First Year Reality

I was petrified to start my third-year medical school obstetrics and gynecology rotation. It was at a hospital in Brooklyn, more than an hour away from my house on Long Island. I had to be there at 6:00 in the morning to make rounds with the residents. Rounding that early meant medical students had to arrive at least a half hour before the rounds started, to do pre-rounds. This was the half hour we had to become familiar with all the patients that would be discussed on rounds at 6:00 with the residents and attending physicians.

We needed to read patient charts, review their labs, and know their histories, so we would be ready to answer any questions that came up during rounds. I could tell on day one that all the residents were exhausted. As the day went on I saw that they seemed overwhelmed and overworked; not one of them seemed happy to be there. No one walked the halls; everyone ran from place to place as if in a constant emergency.

This was a six week rotation, divided into three weeks of gynecology and three weeks of obstetrics. I had to spend every third night in the hospital on a 24-hour shift, remaining in the hospital the following day to go to the out-patient clinic until noon, which amounted to a 30 hour shift. This was in the days before mandatory laws about how many consecutive hours residents could work, but medical students were not even factored into that law. We were often required to stay and work as many hours as anyone with more authority said we should. Above the third year medical students in the hospital hierarchy was just about everyone: fourth year medical students, junior and senior residents, and attendings. There were also many physicians assistants, midwives and nurse practitioners. Keeping track of who did what and who would be teaching me was almost impossible. What was clear was they all obviously knew more than I did.

After my first few confusing days, I realized that most of the staff were just too busy to do any kind of formal teaching. If I wanted to learn, I would have to attach myself to various residents and staff, follow them around as they were running up and down the halls, make myself useful, and try to get some knowledge out of this rotation. I had a strong and natural curiosity to learn about all things in this field for many reasons.

I had always been a strong advocate for women's reproductive rights and freedoms. This might be the chance to see those rights at work. I already had the experience of giving birth, and knew what that process was like at least from a patient point of view, so I was more than curious to see this from the other side. I had also been raised in a family where no one taught me or shared information about the human body or sexuality. I was keenly interested to see how those in the reproductive health field really educated women and girls so they *would* be armed with the proper information on these subjects.

In my home life, Jake was now eight months old. I had had my share of nights getting little-to-no sleep with a fussy nursing baby. I was completely at a loss as to where to find someone I could trust to take care of my baby. I looked at ads, read about agencies, and talked to friends and relatives. I was so afraid that no one would be good enough for me, or for Jake, or—really, how would I *know*?

After a bit of investigating, the best thing that could have happened did happen. A good friend of mine from college told me that her brother was married to a lovely lady from Ireland, a young gal that had moved to the US to take care of her (my friend's) grandmother, then met her (my friend's) brother. She and the brother had started dating. They eventually married, and the grandma passed away.

The wife-caretaker-Irish transplant was available to be a nanny. Not only that, she lived *one* town away from me, and did *not* want a live-in position! I couldn't have asked for more: practically a family member, experienced in caring for others, and wanting a daytime-non-live-in position! I hardly had to interview her.

Charlotte was wonderful, caring, smart, and loving. I knew I had to be comfortable with the idea that my son would need to be cared for and comforted by someone who was not me. I satisfied myself in feeling that if he had more people who could comfort him, rather than fewer people, then the whole separation anxiety thing would be MY problem, not his. I readied myself to go back to the trenches, with a newfound respect for mothers, emotions, needy individuals, and a good night's sleep.

I continued to breastfeed whenever I was home, and to pump bottles during what seemed like all other hours of the day and night. We did switch to disposable diapers. While I didn't mind that something or other was always dripping out of cloth diapers and ruining *my* clothes, I didn't think it fair to impose that on a non-family member.

These next months were the time that I always refer back to when I say that motherhood prepared me for residency. The consistent lack of sleep combined with constantly trying to learn new things, and putting the needs of others before my own were givens in both arenas. Being a third year medical student and having an eight month old at home was a combination that I felt at times very ill-equipped to handle. But again, I got into a pattern, and at least for 6 to 12-week intervals, (the length of time of third year clinical rotations) I felt that same old feeling, 'one thing at a time, and if I could handle this, I could probably handle anything,' I hoped.

But the definition of sleep-deprived hadn't really hit me until I had to leave my house on Long Island at 4:30 in the morning to drive an hour in pitch black darkness and freezing cold, to arrive at the hospital by 5:30 to pre-round. This was truly inhumane.

I knew it would be temporary. I had to just power through. Soon enough I'd be doing something easier, like a family medicine rotation. I started my rotation on the gynecology service. The residents barely addressed the third year medical students except to tell us where to go or what to do, and to look annoyed at us when we did not know the answers to the questions they asked.

I had to know exactly what kind of surgery each patient on the long list of scheduled surgeries was having and why. I had to understand about past histories and the expected outcome of each surgical procedure. I was able to scrub into surgeries where I was holding retractors and trying to stay out of everyone's way. They performed laparoscopic surgeries, tubal ligations, dilation and curettages, and other minor cases that they allowed the third year students to participate in, as long as we had done proper pre-rounding and were familiar with the patients having surgery.

I was shocked to see that once a patient was prepped for surgery, and asleep under general anesthesia in the operating room, no one really seemed to treat the body that was to undergo surgery as if it were a real person. I don't know what I was expecting, but no one had ever explained how they just move patients into the right position for surgery, which sometimes meant up in stirrups, sometimes completely naked, with no regard for patient modesty. The patients were of course unaware, but I thought this strange as there were often people walking in and out of the operating rooms. Students, nurses and residents were there as well.

I later learned that this is very hospital and practitioner dependent. I worked in hospitals where great care and effort was taken for patient modesty, with strategically draped sheets and paper placed over windows while procedures were taking place. I decided immediately that in the future, if it were up to me, then that is exactly what I would do. That just seemed *right*.

Although I at first did not directly address the residents much, I did listen to their conversations. I found out that several of them wanted to go into other medical specialties, orthopedics, or general surgery, but could not find residency spots so they 'settled' for ObGyn. I thought that was so sad, to spend all that time in school and training and then not even go into the field that excited or interested them. And how sad for the patients who had to see a doctor who did not want to be there. I didn't realize at the time how common this was, for residents to go into a field that was not their first or even their second choice because they took the one that was available. I just knew I could not travel that path. If there was some medical specialty I was passionate about, I couldn't fathom doing something completely different.

Toward the end of my second week on this rotation, I met Dr. N, one of the attending doctors. We had an introductory conversation. He asked me about myself, and what my eventual plans were. I told him I really wasn't sure. He surprisingly invited me to scrub in on a surgery he was going to do at the end of the day. It was scheduled for past the time I would have been allowed to leave, but I immediately said 'yes.' This was a hysterectomy. Dr. N told me if I was well-prepared and knew the patient, the history, and the details of the surgery, he might let me do something besides hold a retractor.

I was excited, and went about studying as much as I could, talking to the patient, learning her history, and hearing about her need for the surgery. When we got to the operating room, I felt very prepared.

The OR nurse wheeled the patient in, and I greeted her by name, "Good afternoon, Ms. G, here we are. Are you ready?"

I thought I saw Dr. N smile at that. There was only the attending, a fourth year resident, and me. I had no idea how I got this lucky invitation, but I did not ask. The case was a thing of beauty. From my third year medical student point of view, the surgical technique was impeccable. By the easy chatter and the way Dr. N and the attending operated in sync, it was obvious they had done this many times. There was hardly any blood loss, and Dr. N along with his resident, narrated every part of the case, seemingly for my learning benefit.

"This is the bladder. You see how we need to move it out of the way?" (Who knew that moving a bladder was a thing?) "Look at how large her ovary is." the resident said, displaying it to me. They both asked me various questions along the way: "Tell me the blood supply to the uterus," and "Which ligament gets divided in the first step of a hysterectomy?"

To which I gave the correct answers I had studied that very morning. At every point during this one-hour surgery, I felt like I was falling in love with the beauty of an exquisitely done surgical procedure, with the whole way they were teaching me, and maybe with the resident and the attending themselves. They were the first people on this rotation that were treating me like an actual part of the team. They even showed me how to place a few sutures in the closing part of the operation. I began to consider whether this was a specialty

I might want to apply for when I graduated medical school. I hadn't considered that before.

I never again encountered this exact situation in the operating room during my third year rotation. I still had the obstetrics portion to attend for the next three weeks. I wondered if anything that would happen there might seal the deal for me as far as my interest in obstetrics and gynecology as a potential career choice. That remained to be seen.

Postscript: When I eventually did decide that ObGyn was the field for me, at the end of my residency, I received a call from Dr. R, who was Dr. N's wife. Dr. R was also an ObGyn. She offered me a job right out of residency. I always wondered if that original invitation to join him in the OR so many years before was some kind of a test for the future. Why else would he have smiled when he saw that I had gotten to know the patient before the surgery?

I never asked.

Emthonjeni

Four years after moving from New York to California, I was working as a full time physician at a large state sponsored health clinic. I saw women of all ages for medical and reproductive services. I took a day off in November to have an old filling replaced. Dr. F, our family dentist, was a long-time friend of my husband. He was known for telling lengthy stories as he worked on our teeth. He usually spoke about his son, his grandchildren, and his recent travels. This particular Tuesday, however, Dr. F told me the story of the Flying Dentists.

"Twice a year, a group of us dentists fly to another country where people need dental care, but can't get it in their community," he began. "We bring all our equipment, and set up a temporary dental clinic, spending a few weeks volunteering our services. We've been all over the globe."

Since I had gauze and metal instruments in my open mouth, I could only slightly nod and grunt in polite interest. I was resigned to hearing a full discussion of dental work in underserved communities. This time Dr. F had a different kind of talk in mind. After ten minutes, I realized he was not recounting. He was recruiting!

"Every time we leave one of these communities, we always ask the local program directors what we can bring with us on our next trip that would make it more successful. And every single time, they tell us, 'Please bring a lady doctor who is a *lady doctor*,' he continued.

My thoughts turned from polite interest to minor confusion. If these were flying dentists, did he mean a female dentist? While that was interesting to me, I was not a dentist. I was not yet connecting the dots.

"So our next trip is to South Africa, and I was wondering if you would be interested in coming with us."

Connection made. Dr. F needed a female gynecologist to accompany a group of dentists to a remote spot in South Africa to volunteer to take care of local women while the dentists fixed their teeth. Interesting!

As Dr. F finished my filling, I contemplated the offer. I loved to travel. I believed in volunteering and working in communities in need. I felt positive about working with other volunteers in another country. I would need to know more.

Once my mouth was free, I asked, "When is the trip?"

"The first week of May," he said. "We'll be there for almost three weeks. We even have a safari planned!"

I was intrigued. My intrigue lasted a few minutes until I pulled out my calendar.

"Oh, sorry."

I *knew* that the first week of May was already taken. My son, Jacob, was graduating from college. We had planned a week in Pennsylvania for all the events surrounding the graduation.

"I can't go. We won't be around that week. Sorry."

Dr. F knew I would never miss an important family event. Disappointed but resigned, I assumed that would be the end of the trip for me, at least until the next Flying Dentist adventure. I stood up to go. When I got to the reception desk and was arranging my next cleaning, Dr. F came up behind me.

"Just a question," he started.

I hoped he wasn't going to try to talk me out of attending Jacob's graduation. I turned to face him.

He went on. "When *would* you be able to go?"

I thought for a moment, "Aren't these trips planned very far in advance?" I asked, wondering if he had a different trip already on his calendar.

"Yes," he answered, "But only seven of us are traveling this time. If I can get them to all agree on a different week, when you *can* go, I can try to reschedule."

Wow. I had underestimated the number of times he must have been asked to bring a gynecologist. I knew that lots of planning and coordinating had to go into one of these trips. I pulled out my calendar again.

"Well, since I'll be going away for the week of the graduation, it would have to be a bit distant from that, maybe some time in June?"

He wrote that down. I wasn't sure if I would even be able to get that much time off, but I wanted to go. The thought of traveling, volunteering, *and* a safari? If Dr. F was willing to rearrange the whole trip, I would do what I could to make it happen. I didn't think much more about the possibility.

Three weeks later the loud trill of my phone woke me from a sound sleep.

"Great news!" Dr. F said when I picked up. "We're all set for June first!"

I was suddenly awake.

Had I really said something that sounded like, 'If you change it, I will come?'

He continued excitedly, "I spoke to all my Flying Dentist colleagues, and everyone can go when you can go. I'm so happy! I'll be in touch with the details."

And he hung up.

I closed my eyes. Mild panic set in as I realized I hadn't yet requested time off. I hoped I hadn't made a mistake now that the trip had been arranged to fit into my schedule. I went to work early and headed straight for Human Resources to request the first three weeks of June off, hoping the trip would work out.

I was pleasantly surprised when the person in charge of schedules and benefits said the three weeks would not be a problem. She said that they would be happy to announce the plan in the clinic's monthly newsletter. Sweet relief. Although the trip was seven months away, that afternoon I received an extensive email with 'Flying Dentist Itinerary' in the subject line.

The email had the trip details. I was responsible for my own round trip airfare from San Francisco to Johannesburg, South Africa, but the Flying Dentists would cover all other expenses. We would spend a little over a week in Johannesburg where we would run a dentist-and-gynecology clinic and then another 10 days in Tegula Ferry, a remote village in the mountains. Between the work weeks, we would see elephants and leopards and lions during a safari tour at an animal park. I would work in a hospital in Tegula Ferry while the dentists set up another community dental clinic.

From the wording of the email, I knew this organization had done this orchestration many times before. They had the process down to a science. Also obvious was that they had never had a gynecologist travel with them, so they were unsure what equipment and supplies were required. The suggestion was to 'get started' soliciting the hospitals where I worked and local medical offices and suppliers for donations, and to list everything necessary to run my part of the clinic. This was all up to me. Seven months suddenly did not seem long enough.

I immediately set about making a list of all the necessary supplies. I spent days walking around my own clinic with a notepad. Everything I touched, needed, used, or recommended to my patients went on the list. At the end of three days, the list was four single spaced pages. I wasn't sure that I'd be able to do the most basic medical care without multiple cartons full of supplies. Turned out I had only four months to put my supply cartons together. The plan was to ship everything to South Africa three months before we were to arrive since the travel time for large containers would be long.

I solicited donations from many local offices and clinics, and found them very generous. The labor and delivery unit of the hospital I worked at had many medications, syringes, needles, and tubing they no longer needed. One local dermatology office donated packages of sutures and disposable instruments. My own clinic donated three large boxes of paper drapes and gowns as well as paper to cover exam tables with. I hadn't even thought about table paper!

Over the next four months, I gathered instruments, medications, first aid supplies, and anything needed to do

reasonable and basic exams and procedures on patients. I
hadn't realized how many items might have gone to waste if
I hadn't grabbed them. I received funds to purchase things
that were not donated, like blood pressure cuffs, lamps, and
even a small portable ultrasound machine. My garage was the
organizing station where supplies were catalogued, checked,
and packed into large shipping containers. By March first,
the eight boxes were packed and ready to ship.

Two months before the trip, The Flying Dentists or-
ganized a local meeting for the participants to gather for a
social and educational session. I was eager to meet the other
people traveling to South Africa, and to hear details from
the organizers of the trip. The gathering was in a private
room at a restaurant, and as I entered the conference room,
I immediately recognized Dr. F's wife, Ms. J, sitting at the
far side of a long table. Her eyes met mine, and she gave me
a big smile. I hadn't seen her for about two years.

"Hi!" she exclaimed. "I'm *so* happy you're going on this
trip with us! I'm going to be your assistant!"

I might have looked a bit puzzled, because she continued,
"I'm not sure if you knew that I spent part of my nursing
career working in labor and delivery!"

I was embarrassed to note that I had not even known
she had a nursing career. I always thought of her as the wife
of my dentist when I had seen her at social gatherings. I
knew she was retired, but I didn't know from what. I felt an
immediate sense of relief to think that someone going on
the trip actually had experience in my field. I wouldn't be so
alone in my attempts to care for the women at our make-shift

clinic. I met the rest of the crew that would become my travel companions for the better part of three weeks: three dentists, two dental assistants, Ms. J, and, of course, Dr. F. I listened intently to all the information that was presented about our trip.

Although we were going in June, South Africa would be cold as it was on the opposite side of the equator. We saw pictures of our accommodations at different points in the trip: sparse but adequate. We'd have a three day safari at Kruger Park, one of the biggest safari parks in Africa, where we would stay in cabins. We saw pictures of where we would set up shop, and were given some information about South Africa.

I learned that 11 different languages are spoken there, and that we would have translators with us. We were advised of 'African time,' meaning that life moves more slowly, so expect things to be done at a leisurely pace. I wondered if that was true in a hospital setting. That would take some getting used to. We were warned that the area we would be working in was a high crime area, and because we were going to have medications and medical supplies in our clinic, the local organizers had hired extra security for us. That sounded a little scary. I imagined a small clinic needing armed guards with pit bulls at the doors. Aside from the extra security, these three weeks sounded like a fabulous, intense working vacation. I came home from the meeting thrilled and ready to go.

When D-day finally arrived, I nervously kissed my husband goodbye at the international terminal at San Francisco airport. The first leg of the trip took me to New York, where I met up with some of the other Flying Dentist crew who had flown on a different flight. We then all flew non-stop from Kennedy Airport to Johannesburg, the longest flight I had ever been on. After watching three movies, reading almost an entire book, and getting my usual six hours of sleep, I still had six hours of flying time left. For the last few hours I was too excited to sleep any more, and anxiously and eagerly anticipated landing at O.R. Tambo International Airport. I stared out the window at the drifting cloud formations as we descended, trying not to let my anxiety overtake my excitement.

After going through the security line and customs and immigration, we finally were able to pick up our luggage. I had tried to pack light: lots of scrubs for our days in the clinic and layers of clothing for the nights. We met our hosts at the luggage area, a husband and wife couple. They were super excited to host us. They were young and energetic, speaking South African English, which was both lilting and not always easy to understand.

They loaded us into a medium sized van for our ride to the hotel. Although it was mid afternoon, I could not tell exactly what time of day or what day it was for that matter, after traveling 18 hours and attempting to adjust to a nine hour time difference. I was excited, nervous, hungry, and most of all, jet-lagged. S, one of the dental assistants, was my roommate.

The small Outlook Lodge was a quaint structure, pinkish stucco on the outside like an adobe building in the southwest. A tall woman with short curly hair met us at the front desk.

"Welcome!" she exclaimed in South African English, "You are the docs!"

We smiled back.

We took only a moment to drop our suitcases in our appointed rooms, so the couple that would be our contacts and guides over the next week could take us to a nearby restaurant. The best thing to do was to force my body to accept the new time. If I allowed myself to stay on California time, I would never make the adjustment. I needed to be awake and alert for whatever was to come next. I was grateful there were no patients to see immediately. After trying bobotie, a spicy vegetarian South African treat, and milktart, a pudding in a pie, for dessert, we headed out to the area that was to become our temporary clinic. We needed to set up to see patients the next morning.

Driving through the streets of Johannesburg was a mixture of colorful carnivals. At the same time, often on the same street, we came across distressed and dark enclaves. The carnivals and the enclaves had crowds, loud noises, and scurrying children of all ages, but they were striking in the polar opposite appearances and attitudes of the people in each location. On some streets we saw huge homes, with iron fences around them, and sometimes guards and electrical wires. On others, we saw small shacks with broken windows and peeling paint.

As we got closer to our clinic, the number of crowded, dingy neighborhoods increased. Houses were often made of flimsy cardboard without a sign of indoor plumbing or electricity. Barefoot children ran through muddy puddles, and several times, the smells got the better of us as we drove by with our windows only slightly cracked.

"Most of the people you'll see will come from this surrounding area," K, one of our guides explained, matter-of-factly. "They don't have access to nearby dental, medical, or really any other health services. We have gone into the communities and spoken to people about your traveling dental services, and they will be coming down there starting tomorrow to get the help that they need."

I wondered what kind of gynecology services I would be able to provide to people who hadn't had medical care in a long time, possibly forever. I thought about the supplies I packed, hoping there were things in those cartons that would be useful. I was actually hoping the cartons had arrived. What would I do if they hadn't?

We finally arrived at what appeared to be a large empty grass-covered lot, surrounded by a chain link fence. Right in the middle sat a square stucco building with a narrow dirt road leading up to the doorway. A blue and white mosaic tiled sign was the only bit of color on the outside of the building. The sign said **EMTHONJENI.**

We were told that was the name of the community center, the building where we were going to set up shop. A few local men, women, and children were milling about outside the center, likely curious about what was going to happen. A flock of scrawny chickens was scurrying about, a dog was digging in the dirt, and what looked like a small goat was grazing far out in the field. K dropped us off with the keys, and said she'd be back to pick us up when we called her.

When the door was unlocked, we could see the community center had a large common area, and three smaller side rooms, only one of which had a door that could close all the way. An open room served as a kitchen, with a refrigerator and a stove, and two small bathrooms were in one corner. Furniture was sparse: a few gray folding chairs and two lamps. To my extreme relief, in the middle of the common area, piled on top of each other were all the cartons I had so carefully packed five months earlier. They looked like they had weathered the long trip, mostly intact, although several appeared damaged or opened and re-secured. I was eager to comb through the cartons and coordinate my space.

We immediately looked at each other as if we had the same simultaneous thought.

"The room with the door has to be mine," I said.

I got no argument from anyone. Dentistry could be a public matter; gynecology could not.

I went into the room with the door to see what I would be dealing with. To my happy surprise, I saw two padded tables, which would serve quite well as patient exam tables. I saw a gray metal desk, a wooden chair, lots of shelf space, a sink in the corner, and a small rolling stool to sit on. This might have been a room where some type of therapy had taken place, perhaps massage therapy or physical therapy.

J, who was now my assistant, and I created a usable working space for the next day. We wiped down all the surfaces and pulled a few of the boxes in, looking for the ones labelled 'table paper' and 'sheets and drapes' first. We covered the makeshift exam tables with paper, and put the extra paper and drapes on the accessible shelves. We then systematically emptied cartons, and used all the available shelf and closet space to line up our medications, gloves, instruments, gauze, and other supplies. I had forgotten exactly what I had packed in the cartons, but glad I had thought, so many months earlier, about exactly what I might need to set up shop in an empty room in a non-medical community center. I had packed two headlamps, which I now looked at with relief. The lighting in my exam room was minimal. We had to cover the large windows, which would have been in direct view of people outside, and if I was going to be able to do exams, I'd have to wear a lamp on my head!

Four hours later, when we finished setting up, J and I looked at each other with satisfied relief. The room looked clean. Although simple in detail, we were ready for patients.

When I emerged from the room and peeked at the large common area, I was convinced that everyone else on this trip had done this set up many times before. They had completely transformed the common room into what now looked like a modern professional dental clinic. There were pop-up tables and electrical instruments buzzing and plugged into generators. Reclining dental chairs that must have somehow unfolded from packing boxes were positioned next to the pop-up tables. Instrument sterilizers were spaced around the tables, and an X-ray machine stood against a wall.

The dentists and dental assistants were busily making their way to each station to be sure that there were enough supplies to simultaneously treat two to three patients. A large clear bin with toothbrushes, toothpaste, and dental floss was positioned on a table across from the X-ray machine. A small gray metal desk with new record books, paper, and pens marked the intake area near the entrance. That would be where patients could state their problems. The intake person would track everyone we would see and their treatments.

We had taken four hours to transform an empty community center into what was about to become a fully functional dental-and-gynecology community clinic. I was in awe of what the Flying Dentists had accomplished, and excited with anticipation.

K told us that they had posted signs about the clinic in Zulu and Sesotho in the town. Opening day was to be the next day, starting at 9:00 in the morning. This was a walk-in clinic, first come, first served. After setting up the entire community center to accommodate patients, our crew was understandably exhausted. We agreed that once we were done with the rooms, we would go back to our hotel for dinner and a good night's sleep. We took a few steps back, admiring our set-up. K returned to pick us up. She looked truly amazed at the total transformation of the space.

As we gathered up our things to go, we heard a loud knock on the door. K opened it. She thought we would file out to the van, but we now saw two young women standing outside. They were both thin, South African women with large eyes and pleading expressions. The younger of the two appeared about 18. She was leaning on the other woman, standing in such a way that her pain was obvious. She wore a multicolored sundress and was barefoot. The other woman appeared to be her caretaker, and immediately began talking to K in Zulu.

After a few minutes of animated conversation, K turned and addressed me.

"They are two sisters who live about three miles away. They heard that there was a gynecologist here, and came to see if you can help the younger sister. She has some kind of problem 'down there' and hasn't been able to walk properly for months. She hasn't been able to see a doctor, and is too embarrassed to tell anyone."

We weren't really ready to see any patients at that very moment, but I could not turn her away. I spoke to the rest of the crew. If they were willing to wait while I took this first patient into my newly prepared exam room, I would assess the situation to see if I could help.

They agreed to wait. We could not turn the two women away. The rest of the crew settled into the dental recliners to wait. J and I helped the two into my newly-created gynecology exam room, and K came in to be our translator. I had the younger woman lay down on the exam table while I washed my hands, placed one of my headlamps on my head, and put on latex gloves.

"Please let her know that I need to take a look at the problem to decide if I can help her."

K translated this, and the young woman nodded. J placed a chair near the head of the table so her sister could sit and hold her hand. The younger sister was wearing only the sundress, with nothing underneath. Through translation, she relayed that she had been unable to wear anything else because she was in so much pain for the past three months.

When I gently lifted the dress, I saw a large inflamed fluctuant, angry looking pus-filled abscess, about the size of a tennis ball, pressing on her groin and blocking her vaginal opening. I could see how uncomfortable she must be, and how this prevented her from walking properly or wearing anything that would touch this area. The solution to this would be to drain it. I explained, and K translated, what I would need to do. I assured them that I could use something local to numb it, but it might still be uncomfortable. She squeezed her sister's hand, but nodded in agreement.

J and I got out the supplies that we needed: local anesthetic, a syringe, needle, a disposable scalpel, an antiseptic cleanser, and packing. I also relayed that we would give her a shot of an antibiotic, and J got that ready as well. With J's assistance, I gently swabbed the abscess area with an antiseptic cleanser, then injected it with the smallest needle and an abundance of local anesthetic. She winced, but only for a moment. I could not imagine this pain was any worse than what she'd been feeling for the last few months.

Once the area was completely numb, I made a stab incision in it with my scalpel, and watched as copious amounts of thick pus and fluid drained out of it onto my carefully placed drapes and gauze pads. Once the abscess was completely drained and empty, I explained to K, who translated, that I would have to leave a small drain inside it. Over the next few days fluid would continue to drain, and the drain would prevent it from filling up again.

The sisters nodded in agreement, and said they understood. I loosely taped a gauze pad over the drain. The young woman seemed shocked to see how easily she could move to a sitting position. Then she got up from the table and walked, moving naturally and without pain. Her eyes filled with tears, and she said something softly to K, who then translated that this was the first time in months that she was not suffering. She was grateful. I smiled, and the young woman hugged me.

In clear English, she said, "Thank you."

I teared up as well. J gave her an injection of ceftriaxone, an antibiotic, and we gave them instructions and told them to return in two days so I could recheck the area.

After they left, J and I cleaned up, and readied the room for the next day, which was truly the opening day of our clinic.

"At least now I can tell that the things I packed seem to be the right ones for the job," I remarked. "Hope we have enough supplies if we'll be seeing things like that every day!"

J answered, "I hope so too."

The next morning, the van picked us up from the Outlook Lodge at 8:00. We piled in, ready for our first full day in the clinic.

The driver excitedly said "Good morning docs! Welcome! I heard some news about you guys in town last night! People are talking!"

He didn't elaborate but I hoped that was good news. I looked out the window as we drove through town to Emthonjeni. I noted the same mix of colorful and dingy neighborhoods and recognized the route we were taking to reach our clinic. At 8:20 when we reached the chain-link fence that surrounded the clinic building, I absolutely had my answer to the nature of the 'in-town' discussions that people must have been having. Starting at the community center door, where the sign clearly read, "OPEN AT 9:00

AM," I saw a line of at least thirty people. Most were women. A few were obviously pregnant. Some were standing, some had brought chairs. Some were sitting on the ground. Some were chatting. The line snaked almost all the way to the road where we had entered. When we got out of the van, many people turned to look at us.

Some pointed, and some started chanting: "Lady doc, lady doc."

I was overcome when I realized that the tale of last night's minor procedure at the clinic had somehow made its way through the local area, and many community members must need or want some similar service from me today. I smiled at the line-up.

I looked at J and exclaimed, "This is going to be a great day. Let's get to work."

Thank You

This has been a most difficult year to relay stories of joy, heartbreak, sympathy, and empathy. In 2020 and part of 2021, the inability to touch and hug, to shake hands, and to high-five has limited my ability to share incredible moments with my patients. Through my words, I hope I have been able to relay how emotional these episodes have been. Smiles and tears can still be obvious behind a mask.

As we return to more normalcy in medicine as in all other avenues of our lives, I will continue to tell the stories that have affected me. More stories are *always* there.

My most heartfelt thanks to everyone who helped get this book written and published. I am forever grateful.

- To all the patients who have entrusted me with their care and allowed me to write about their experiences,
- To my family who had to listen to each story in various forms and iterations until I felt I finally got it right,
- To Lili Garcia, CNM, NP, who has helped lighten my clinical load so I was able to write,
- To Shelly Hanan, the first friend I made in California, for making me look good with your amazing photos,
- To Inda Shirley, who has the uncanny ability to help make my words say what I was trying to say in the first place, but better.

Made in the USA
Middletown, DE
27 September 2023

39336740R00086